Glencoe Mathematics

Geometry

Chapter 12
Resource Masters

Glencoe

New York, New York   Columbus, Ohio   Chicago, Illinois   Peoria, Illinois   Woodland Hills, California

Consumable Workbooks Many of the worksheets contained in the Chapter Resource Masters are available as consumable workbooks in both English and Spanish.

	ISBN10	ISBN13
Study Guide and Intervention Workbook	0-07-877344-X	978-0-07-877344-0
Skills Practice Workbook	0-07-877346-6	978-0-07-877346-4
Practice Workbook	0-07-877347-4	978-0-07-877347-1
Word Problem Practice Workbook	0-07-877349-0	978-0-07-877349-5
Spanish Versions		
Study Guide and Intervention Workbook	0-07-877345-8	978-0-07-877345-7
Practice Workbook	0-07-877348-2	978-0-07-877348-8

Answers for Workbooks The answers for Chapter 12 of these workbooks can be found in the back of this Chapter Resource Masters booklet.

StudentWorks Plus™ This CD-ROM includes the entire Student Edition test along with the English workbooks listed above.

TeacherWorks Plus™ All of the materials found in this booklet are included for viewing, printing, and editing in this CD-ROM.

Spanish Assessment Masters (ISBN10: 0-07-877350-4, ISBN13: 978-0-07-877350-1) These masters contain a Spanish version of Chapter 12 Test Form 2A and Form 2C.

 Glencoe

The McGraw·Hill Companies

Send all inquiries to:
Glencoe/McGraw-Hill
8787 Orion Place
Columbus, OH 43240

ISBN13: 978-0-07-873969-9
ISBN10: 0-07-873969-1

Geometry CRM12

Printed in the United States of America

3 4 5 6 7 8 9 10 009 13 12 11 10 09 08

CONTENTS

Teacher's Guide to Using the Chapter 12 Resource Masters

The *Chapter 12 Resource Masters* includes the core materials needed for Chapter 12. These materials include worksheets, extensions, and assessment options. The answers for these pages appear at the back of this booklet.

All of the materials found in this booklet are included for viewing and printing on the *TeacherWorks Plus*™ CD-ROM.

Chapter Resources

Student-Built Glossary (pages 1–2) These masters are a student study tool that presents up to twenty of the key vocabulary terms from the chapter. Students are to record definitions and/or examples for each term. You may suggest that students highlight or star the terms with which they are not familiar. Give this to students before beginning Lesson 12–1. Encourage them to add these pages to their mathematics study notebooks. Remind them to complete the appropriate words as they study each lesson.

Anticipation Guide (pages 7–8) This master, presented in both English and Spanish, is a survey used before beginning the chapter to pinpoint what students may or may not know about the concepts in the chapter. Students will revisit this survey after they complete the chapter to see if their perceptions have changed.

Lesson Resources

Lesson Reading Guide Get Ready for the Lesson extends the discussion from the beginning of the Student Edition lesson. Read the Lesson asks students to interpret the context of and relationships among terms in the lesson. Finally, Remember What You Learned asks students to summarize what they have learned using various representation techniques. Use as a study tool for note taking or as an informal reading assignment. It is also a helpful tool for ELL (English Language Learners).

Study Guide and Intervention These masters provide vocabulary, key concepts, additional worked-out examples and Check Your Progress exercises to use as a reteaching activity. It can also be used in conjunction with the Student Edition as an instructional tool for students who have been absent.

Skills Practice This master focuses more on the computational nature of the lesson. Use as an additional practice option or as homework for second-day teaching of the lesson.

Practice This master closely follows the types of problems found in the Exercises section of the Student Edition and includes word problems. Use as an additional practice option or as homework for second-day teaching of the lesson.

Word Problem Practice This master includes additional practice in solving word problems that apply the concepts of the lesson. Use as an additional practice or as homework for second-day teaching of the lesson.

Enrichment These activities may extend the concepts of the lesson, offer a historical or multicultural look at the concepts, or widen students' perspectives on the mathematics they are learning. They are written for use with all levels of students.

Graphing Calculator, Scientific Calculator, or Spreadsheet Activities

These activities present ways in which technology can be used with the concepts in some lessons of this chapter. Use as an alternative approach to some concepts or as an integral part of your lesson presentation.

Assessment Options

The assessment masters in the *Chapter 12 Resource Masters* offer a wide range of assessment tools for formative (monitoring) assessment and summative (final) assessment.

Student Recording Sheet This master corresponds with the standardized test practice at the end of the chapter.

Pre-AP Rubric This master provides information for teachers and students on how to assess performance on open-ended questions.

Quizzes Four free-response quizzes offer assessment at appropriate intervals in the chapter.

Mid-Chapter Test This 1-page test provides an option to assess the first half of the chapter. It parallels the timing of the Mid-Chapter Quiz in the Student Edition and includes both multiple-choice and free-response questions.

Vocabulary Test This test is suitable for all students. It includes a list of vocabulary words and 10 questions to assess students' knowledge of those words. This can also be used in conjunction with one of the leveled chapter tests.

Leveled Chapter Tests

- *Form 1* contains multiple-choice questions and is intended for use with below grade level students.
- *Forms 2A and 2B* contain multiple-choice questions aimed at on grade level students. These tests are similar in format to offer comparable testing situations.
- *Forms 2C and 2D* contain free-response questions aimed at on grade level students. These tests are similar in format to offer comparable testing situations.
- *Form 3* is a free-response test for use with above grade level students.

All of the above mentioned tests include a free-response Bonus question.

Extended-Response Test Performance assessment tasks are suitable for all students. Sample answers and a scoring rubric are included for evaluation.

Standardized Test Practice These three pages are cumulative in nature. It includes three parts: multiple-choice questions with bubble-in answer format, griddable questions with answer grids, and short-answer free-response questions.

Answers

- The answers for the Anticipation Guide and Lesson Resources are provided as reduced pages with answers appearing in red.
- Full-size answer keys are provided for the assessment masters.

12 Student-Built Glossary

This is an alphabetical list of the key vocabulary terms you will learn in Chapter 12. As you study the chapter, complete each term's definition or description. Remember to add the page number where you found the term. Add these pages to your Geometry Study Notebook to review vocabulary at the end of the chapter.

Vocabulary Term	Found on Page	Definition/Description/Example
axis		
circular cone		
corner view		
cross section		
great circle		
hemisphere		
lateral area		
lateral edges		
lateral faces		

(continued on the next page)

12 Student-Built Glossary (continued)

Vocabulary Term	Found on Page	Definition/Description/Example
oblique cone		
perspective view		
reflection symmetry		
regular pyramid		
right cone		
right cyllinder		
right prism (PRIZ·uhm)		
slant height		

12 Anticipation Guide

Extending Surface Area

Step 1 *Before you begin Chapter 12*

• Read each statement.

• Decide whether you Agree (A) or Disagree (D) with the statement.

• Write A or D in the first column OR if you are not sure whether you agree or disagree, write NS (Not Sure).

STEP 1 A, D, or NS	Statement	STEP 2 A or D
	1. Prisms, pyramids, cylinders, and cones are all polyhedrons.	
	2. The net of a pyramid could contain a square and four triangles.	
	3. The lateral area of a prism is equal to the sum of the areas of each face.	
	4. The axis of an oblique cylinder is different than the height of the cylinder.	
	5. The surface area of a right cylinder with radius r and height h is $2\pi rh + 2\pi r^2$.	
	6. The slant height and height of a regular pyramid are the same.	
	7. Since a pyramid has only one base, its surface area equals its lateral area.	
	8. The lateral area of a cone equals the product of π, the radius, and the height of the cone.	
	9. To find the surface area of a sphere with radius r, multiply πr^2 by 4.	
	10. A *great circle* of a sphere is any circle formed by the intersection of a plane and the sphere.	

Step 2 *After you complete Chapter 12*

• Reread each statement and complete the last column by entering an A or a D.

• Did any of your opinions about the statements change from the first column?

• For those statements that you mark with a D, use a piece of paper to write an example of why you disagree.

12 Ejercicios preparatorios

Extiende el área de superficie

PASO 1   *Antes de comenzar el Capítulo 12*

- Lee cada enunciado.
- Decide si estás de acuerdo (A) o en desacuerdo (D) con el enunciado.
- Escribe A o D en la primera columna O si no estás seguro(a) de la respuesta, escribe NS (No estoy seguro(a).

PASO 1 A, D o NS	Enunciado	PASO 2 A o D
	1. Los prismas, las pirámides, los cilindros y los conos son poliedros.	
	2. La red de una pirámide podría contener un cuadrado y cuatro triángulos.	
	3. El área lateral de un prisma es igual a la suma de las áreas de cada cara.	
	4. El eje de un cilindro oblicuo es diferente a la altura del cilindro.	
	5. El área de superficie de un cilindro recto con radio r y altura h es $2\pi rh + 2\pi r^2$.	
	6. La altura oblicua y la altura de una pirámide regular son las mismas.	
	7. Dado que una pirámide tiene una sola base, su área de superficie es igual a su área lateral.	
	8. El área lateral de un cono es igual al producto de π, el radio, por la altura del cono.	
	9. Para calcular el área de superficie de una esfera con radio r, multiplica πr^2 por 4.	
	10. El *gran círculo* de una esfera es cualquier círculo que se forma por la intersección de un plano y la esfera.	

PASO 2   *Después de completar el Capítulo 12*

- Vuelve a leer cada enunciado y completa la última columna con una A o una D.
- ¿Cambió cualquiera de tus opiniones sobre los enunciados de la primera columna?
- En una hoja de papel aparte, escribe un ejemplo de por qué estás en desacuerdo con los enunciados que marcaste con una D.

12-1 Lesson Reading Guide

Representations of Three-Dimensional Figures

Get Ready For the Lesson

Read the introduction to Lesson 12-1 in your textbook.

Artists use three-point perspective to draw three-dimensional objects with a high degree of realism. Why do three-point perspective drawings look more realistic than isometric drawings?

Read the Lesson

Complete the following table.

Word	Definition
1. corner view	
2. perspective view	
3. cross section	
4. reflection symmetry	

5. A three-point perspective drawing has three _____ points. Each of these points is aligned with the _____, width, and length of the figure.

6. A cross section of a solid occurs when a _____ intersects a solid figure.

Remember What You Learned

7. Look up the word isometry in a dictionary. Compare its definition with the definition of corner view and perspective view. Why are corner views considered isometric views but three-dimensional point perspective views not considered isometric views?

12-1 Study Guide and Intervention (continued)

Representations of Three-Dimensional Figures

Drawings of Three-Dimensional Figures To work with a three-dimensional object, it can be useful to draw different views. The view of a figure from a corner is called the **corner view** or **perspective view**. An orthographic drawing includes a two-dimensional top view, left view, front view, and right view of a three-dimensional.

Example 1 Use isometric dot paper to sketch a triangular prism with 3-4-5 right triangles as bases and with a height of 3 units.

Step 1 Draw $\overline{AB}$ at 3 units and draw $\overline{AC}$ at 4 units.

Step 2 Draw $\overline{AD}$, $\overline{BE}$, and $\overline{CF}$, each at 3 units.

Step 3 Draw $\overline{BC}$ and $\triangle DEF$.

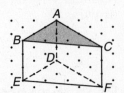

Example 2 Draw the back view of the figure given the orthogonal drawing.

• The top view indicates two columns.

• The right and left views indicate that the height of figure is three blocks.

• The front view indicates that the columns have heights 2 and 3 blocks.

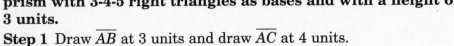

Use blocks to make a model of the object. Then use your model to draw the back view. The back view indicates that the columns have heights 3 and 2 blocks.

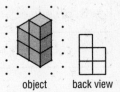

Exercises

Sketch each solid using isometric dot paper.

1. cube with edge 4

2. rectangular prism 1 unit high, 5 units long, and 4 units wide

Draw the back view and corner view of a figure given each orthographic drawing.

3.

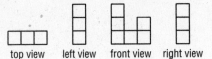

4.

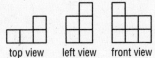

12-1 Study Guide and Intervention (continued)

Representations of Three-Dimensional Figures

Cross-Sections The intersection of a solid and a plane is called a cross-section of the solid. The shape of a cross-section depends upon the shape of the solid figure, the angle of the plane makes with the base of the solid figure, and where the plane interests the figure.

Example

There are several interesting shapes that are cross-sections of a cone. Determine the shape resulting from each cross-section of the cone.

a.
If the plane is parallel to the base of the cone, then the resulting cross-section will be a circle.

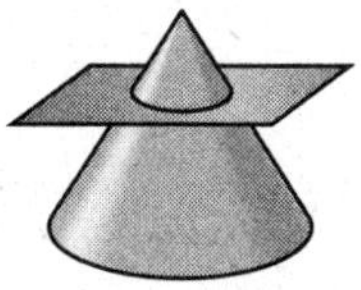

Top View

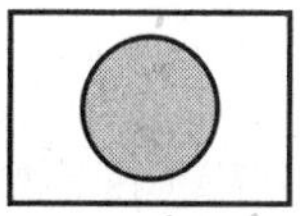

b.
If the plane cuts through the cone perpendicular to the base and through the center of the cone, then the resulting cross-section will be a triangle.

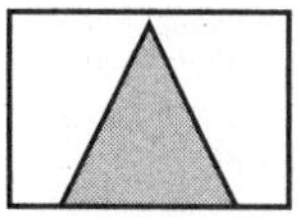

Side View

c.
If the plane cuts across the entire cone, then the resulting cross-section will be an ellipse.

Angle View

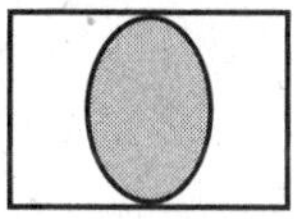

Exercises

Determine the shape resulting from each cross section of the cylinder.

1.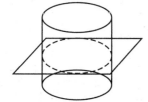

2.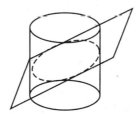

3.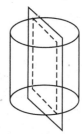

Lesson 12-1

12-1 Skills Practice

Representations of Three-Dimensional Figures

Sketch each solid using isometric dot paper.

1. cube 2 units on each edge

2. rectangular prism 2 units high, 5 units long, and 2 units wide

Draw the back view and corner view of a figure given each orthogonal drawing.

3.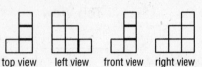

top view   left view   front view   right view

4.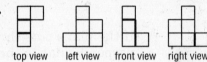

top view   left view   front view   right view

Determine the shape resulting from each cross section of the square prism.

5.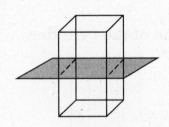

6.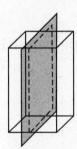

7.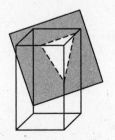

8.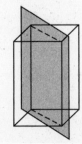

12-1 Practice

Representations of Three-Dimensional Figures

Sketch each solid using isometric dot paper.

1. rectangular prism 3 units high, 3 units long, and 2 units wide

2. triangular prism 3 units high, whose bases are right triangles with legs 2 units and 4 units long

Draw the back view and corner view of a figure given each orthogonal drawing.

3.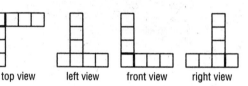

4.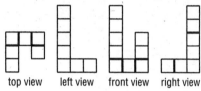

Determine the cross-section resulting from the horizontal and vertical slice of each solid.

5.

6.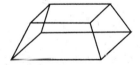

7. **SPHERES** Consider the sphere in Exercise 5. Based on the cross-section resulting from the horizontal and vertical slice of the sphere, make a conjecture about all spherical cross-sections.

8. **MINERALS** Pyrite, also known as fool's gold, can form crystals that are perfect cubes. Suppose a gemologist wants to cut a cube of pyrite to get a square and a rectanglar face. What cuts should be made to get each of the shapes? Illustrate your answers.

Lesson 12-1

12-1 **Word Problem Practice**

Representations of Three-Dimensional Figures

1. **LABELS** Jamal removes the label from a cylindrical soup can to earn points for his school. Sketch the shape of the label.

2. **BLOCKS** Margot's three-year-old son made the magnetic block sculpture shown below in corner view.

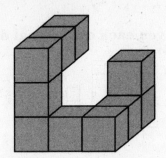

Draw the right view of the sculpture.

3. **CUBES** Nathan marks the midpoints of three edges of a cube as shown. He then slices the cube along a plane that contains these three points. Describe the resulting cross section.

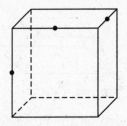

4. **ENGINEERING** Stephanie needs an object whose top view is a circle and whose left and front views are squares. Describe an object that will satisfy these conditions.

DESK SUPPORTS For Exercises 5-7, use the following information.
The figure shows the support for a desk.

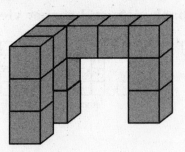

5. Draw the top view.

6. Draw the front view.

7. Draw the right view.

12-1 Enrichment

Drawing Solids on Isometric Dot Paper

Isometric dot paper is helpful for drawing solids. Remember to use dashed lines for hidden edges.

For each solid shown, draw another solid whose dimensions are twice as large.

1.

2.

3.

4.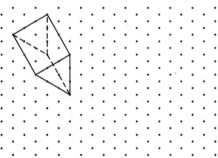

5.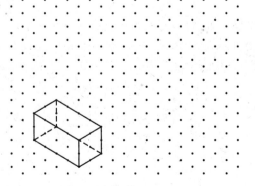

6.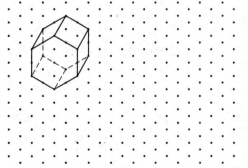

Lesson 12-1

12-1 Graphing Calculator Activity

Perspective Drawings

The science of perspective drawing studies how to draw a three-dimensional object on a two-dimensional page. This science became highly refined during the Renaissance with the work of artists such as Albrecht Dürer and Leonardo da Vinci.

Today, computers are often used to make perspective drawings, particularly elaborate graphics used in television and movies. The three-dimensional coordinates of objects are figured. Then algebra is used to transform these into two-dimensional coordinates. The graph of these new coordinates is called a *projection*.

The formulas below will draw one type of projection in which the y-axis is drawn horizontally, the z-axis vertically, and the x-axis at an angle of $a°$ with the y-axis. If the three-dimensional coordinates of a point are (x, y, z), then the projection coordinates (X, Y) are given by

$$X = x(-\cos a) + y \text{ and } Y = x(-\sin a) + z.$$

Although this type of projection gives a fairly good perspective drawing, it does distort some lengths.

1. The drawing with the coordinates given below is a cube.

   $A(5, 0, 5), B(5, 5, 5), C(5, 5, 0), D(5, 0, 0),$
   $E(0, 0, 5), F(0, 5, 5), G(0, 5, 0), H(0, 0, 0)$

   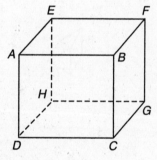

   Use the formulas above to find the projection coordinates of each point, using $a = 45$. Round projection coordinates to the nearest integer. Graph the cube on a graphing calculator. Make a sketch of the display.

   $A'(\_\_, \_\_)\ B'(\_\_, \_\_)\ C'(\_\_, \_\_)\ D'(\_\_, \_\_)\ E'(\_\_, \_\_)\ F'(\_\_, \_\_)$
   $G'(\_\_, \_\_)\ H'(\_\_, \_\_)$

2. The points $A(10, 2, 0), B(10, 10, 0), C(2, 10, 0),$ and $D(3, 3, 4)$ are vertices of a pyramid. Find the projection coordinates, using $a = 25$. Round coordinates to the nearest integer. Then graph the pyramid on a graphing calculator by drawing $\overline{A'B'}, \overline{B'C'}, \overline{C'D'}, \overline{D'A'}$, and $\overline{D'B'}$. Make a sketch of the display.

   $A'(\_\_, \_\_)\ B'(\_\_, \_\_)\ C'(\_\_, \_\_)\ D'(\_\_, \_\_)$

12

12-2 Lesson Reading Guide
Surface Areas of Prisms

Get Ready for the Lesson

Read the introduction to Lesson 12-2 in your textbook.

How could the architects figure out lateral area of the building?

Read the Lesson

1. Determine whether each sentence is *always*, *sometimes*, or *never* true.

   a. A base of a prism is a face of the prism.
   b. A face of a prism is a base of the prism.
   c. The lateral faces of a prism are rectangles.
   d. If a base of a prism has n vertices, then the prism has n faces.
   e. If a base of a prism has n vertices, then the prism has n lateral edges.
   f. In a right prism, the lateral edges are also altitudes.
   g. The bases of a prism are congruent regular polygons.
   h. Any two lateral edges of a prism are perpendicular to each other.
   i. In a rectangular prism, any pair of opposite faces can be called the bases.
   j. All of the lateral faces of a prism are congruent to each other.

2. Explain the difference between the *lateral area* of a prism and the *surface area* of a prism. Your explanation should apply to both right and oblique prisms. Do not use any formulas in your explanation.

3. Refer to the figure.

   a. Name this solid with as specific a name as possible.

   b. Name the bases of the solid.
   c. Name the lateral faces.

   d. Name the edges.
   e. Name an altitude of the solid.
   f. If a represents the area of one of the bases, P represents the perimeter of one of the bases, and $x = AF$, write an expression for the surface area of the solid that involves a, P, and x.

Remember What You Learned

4. A good way to remember a new mathematical term is to relate it to an everyday use of the same word. How can the way the word *lateral* is used in sports help you remember the meaning of the *lateral area* of a solid?

12-2 Study Guide and Intervention *(continued)*
Surface Areas of Prisms

Lateral Areas of Prisms Here are some characteristics of prisms.

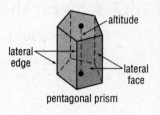

pentagonal prism

• The bases are parallel and congruent.
• The **lateral faces** are the faces that are not bases.
• The lateral faces intersect at **lateral edges**, which are parallel.
• The **altitude** of a prism is a segment that is perpendicular to the bases with an endpoint in each base.
• For a **right prism**, the lateral edges are perpendicular to the bases. Otherwise, the prism is **oblique**.

Lateral Area of a Prism	If a prism has a lateral area of L square units, a height of h units, and each base has a perimeter of P units, then $L = Ph$.

Example Find the lateral area of the regular pentagonal prism above if each base has a perimeter of 75 centimeters and the altitude is 10 centimeters.

$L = Ph$ Lateral area of a prism
$\quad = 75(10)$ $P = 75, h = 10$
$\quad = 750$ Multiply.

The lateral area is 750 square centimeters.

Exercises

Find the lateral area of each prism.

1.

2.
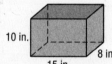

3.

4.
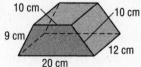

5.
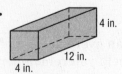

6.
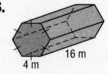

12-2 Study Guide and Intervention *(continued)*

Surface Areas of Prisms

Surface Areas of Prisms The surface area of a prism is the lateral area of the prism plus the areas of the bases.

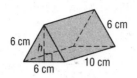

Surface Area of a Prism	If the total surface area of a prism is T square units, its height is h units, and each base has an area of B square units and a perimeter of P units, then $T = L + 2B$.

Example **Find the surface area of the triangular prism above.**

Find the lateral area of the prism.

$L = Ph$ Lateral area of a prism
$ = (18)(10)$ $P = 18, h = 10$
$ = 180 \text{ cm}^2$ Multiply.

Find the area of each base. Use the Pythagorean Theorem to find the height of the triangular base.

$h^2 + 3^2 = 6^2$ Pythagorean Theorem
$ h^2 = 27$ Simplify.
$ h = 3\sqrt{3}$ Take the square root of each side.
$B = \frac{1}{2} \times \text{base} \times \text{height}$ Area of a triangle
$ = \frac{1}{2}(6)(3\sqrt{3}) \text{ or } 15.6 \text{ cm}^2$

The total area is the lateral area plus the area of the two bases.

$T = 180 + 2(15.6)$ Substitution
$ = 211.2 \text{ cm}^2$ Simplify.

Exercises

Find the surface area of each prism. Round to the nearest tenth if necessary.

1.
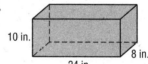

2.

3.
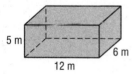

4.

5.
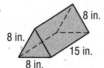

6.

Lesson 12-2

12-2 **Skills Practice**

Surface Areas of Prisms

Find the lateral area of each prism.

1.

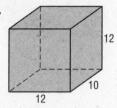

2.

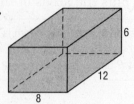

3.

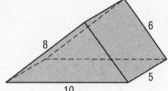

4.

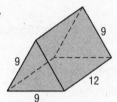

Find the surface area of each prism. Round to the nearest tenth if necessary.

5.

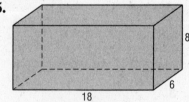

6.

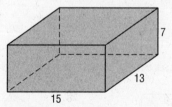

7.

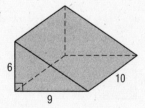

8.

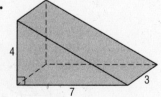

12-2 Practice

Surface Areas of Prisms

Find the lateral area of each prism. Round to the nearest tenth if necessary.

1.
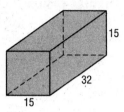
15
32
15

2.
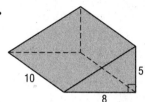
10
8
5

3.
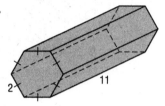
2
11

4.
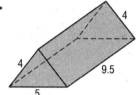
4
4
9.5
5

Find the surface area of each prism. Round to the nearest tenth if necessary.

5.
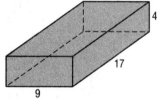
4
17
9

6.

13
6
7

7.
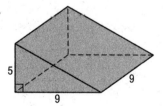
5
9
9

8.
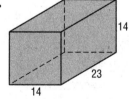
14
23
14

9. **CRAFTS** Becca made a rectangular jewelry box in her art class and plans to cover it in red silk. If the jewelry box is $6\frac{1}{2}$ inches long, $4\frac{1}{2}$ inches wide, and 3 inches high, find the surface area that will be covered.

12-2 Word Problem Practice

Surface Areas of Prisms

1. LOGOS The Z company specializes in caring for zebras. They want to make a 3-dimensional "Z" to put in front of their company headquarters. The "Z" is 15 inches thick and the perimeter of the base is 390 inches.

15"

What is the lateral surface area of this "Z"?

2. STAIRWELLS Management decides to enclose stairs connecting the first and second floors of a parking garage in a stairwell shaped like an oblique rectangular prism.

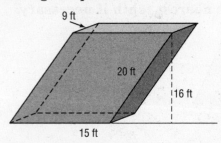

9 ft

20 ft

16 ft

15 ft

What is the lateral surface area of the stairwell?

3. CAKES A cake is a rectangular prism with height 4 inches and base 12 inches by 15 inches. Wallace wants to apply frosting to the sides and the top of the cake. What is the surface area of the part of the cake that will have frosting?

4. CANDY A candy maker packages one of its products in a triangular prism. The height of the prism is 10 inches. The base is an equilateral triangle with side length 3 inches. What is the surface area of the package? Round your answer to the nearest hundredth.

WOOD PLANKS For Exercises 5-8, use the following information.

A wood plank is a rectangular prism with length 10 feet and base dimensions 2 inches by 4 inches.

5. What is the surface area of the plank in square inches?

6. Katrina cuts the plank in half lengthwise and obtains two wood planks, each 5 feet long. What is the total surface area of both planks?

7. If instead, Katrina had cut the plank into N equal pieces lengthwise, what would be the total surface area of all N pieces?

8. Katrina wants to cut the plank into two rectangular pieces in a way that will give her the greatest total surface area for the pieces. How should she cut the plank?

12-2 **Enrichment**

Cross Sections of Prisms

When a plane intersects a solid figure to form a two-dimensional figure, the results is called a **cross section**. The figure at the right shows a plane intersecting a cube. The cross section is a hexagon.

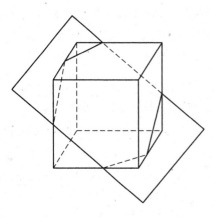

For each right prism, connect the labeled points in alphabetical order to show a cross section. Then identify the polygon.

1.

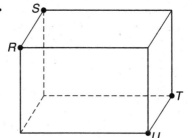

2.

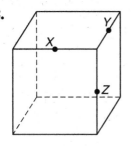

3.

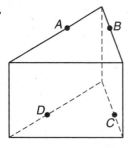

Refer to the right prisms shown at the right. In the rectangular prism, A and C are midpoints. Identify the cross-section polygon formed by a plane containing the given points.

4. A, C, H

5. C, E, G

6. H, C, E, F

7. H, A, E

8. B, D, F

9. V, X, R

10. R, T, Y

11. R, S, W

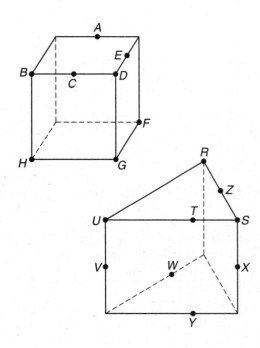

12-3 Lesson Reading Guide
Surface Areas of Cylinders

Get Ready for the Lesson

Read the introduction to Lesson 12-3 in your textbook.

If the surface area of the half-pipe includes an added flat section in the middle, then how does the surface area of the half-pipe compare to the full-pipe?

Read the Lesson

1. Underline the correct word or phrase to form a true statement.

   a. The bases of a cylinder are (rectangles/regular polygons/circles).

   b. The (axis/radius/diameter) of a cylinder is the segment whose endpoints are the centers of the bases.

   c. The net of a cylinder is composed of two congruent (rectangles/circles) and one (rectangle/semicircle).

   d. In a right cylinder, the axis of the cylinder is also a(n) (base/lateral edge/altitude).

   e. A cylinder that is not a right cylinder is called an (acute/obtuse/oblique) cylinder.

2. Match each description from the first column with an expression from the second column that represents its value.

   a. the lateral area of a right cylinder in which the radius of each base is x cm and the length of the axis is y cm

   b. the surface area of a right prism with square bases in which the length of a side of a base is x cm and the length of a lateral edge is y cm

   c. the surface area of a right cylinder in which the radius of a base is x cm and the height is y cm

   d. the surface area of regular hexahedron (cube) in which the length of each edge is x cm

   e. the lateral area of a triangular prism in which the bases are equilateral triangles with side length x cm and the height is y cm

   f. the surface area of a right cylinder in which the diameter of the base is x cm and the length of the axis is y cm

   i. $(2x^2 + 4xy)$ cm^2

   ii. $(2\pi xy + 2\pi x^2)$ cm^2

   iii. $3xy$ cm^2

   iv. $6x^2$ cm^2

   v. $2\pi xy$ cm^2

   vi. $\left(\dfrac{\pi x^2}{2} + \pi xy\right)$ cm^2

Remember What You Learned

3. Often the best way to remember a mathematical formula is to think about where the different parts of the formula come from. How can you use this approach to remember the formula for the surface area of a cylinder?

12-3 Study Guide and Intervention

Surface Areas of Cylinders

Lateral Areas of Cylinders A **cylinder** is a solid whose bases are congruent circles that lie in parallel planes. The **axis** of a cylinder is the segment whose endpoints are the centers of these circles. For a **right cylinder**, the axis and the altitude of the cylinder are equal. The lateral area of a right cylinder is the circumference of the cylinder multiplied by the height.

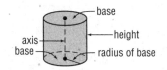

Lateral Area of a Cylinder	If a cylinder has a lateral area of L square units, a height of h units, and the bases have radii of r units, then $L = 2\pi rh$.

Example Find the lateral area of the cylinder above if the radius of the base is 6 centimeters and the height is 14 centimeters.

$L = 2\pi rh$ Lateral area of a cylinder
$\ \ = 2\pi(6)(14)$ Substitution
$\ \ \approx 527.8$ Simplify.

The lateral area is about 527.8 square centimeters.

Exercises

Find the lateral area of each cylinder. Round to the nearest tenth.

1.

4 cm
12 cm

2.

10 in. 6 in.

3.

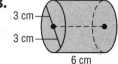

3 cm
3 cm
6 cm

4.

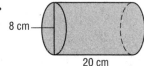

8 cm
20 cm

5.

12 m
4 m

6.

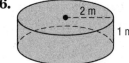

2 m
1 m

12-3 Study Guide and Intervention *(continued)*

Surface Areas of Cylinders

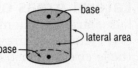

Surface Areas of Cylinders The surface area of a cylinder is the lateral area of the cylinder plus the areas of the bases.

Surface Area of a Cylinder	If a cylinder has a surface area of T square units, a height of h units, and the bases have radii of r units, then $T = 2\pi rh + 2\pi r^2$.

Example **Find the surface area of the cylinder.**

Find the lateral area of the cylinder. If the diameter is 12 centimeters, then the radius is 6 centimeters.

$$L = Ph \qquad \text{Lateral area of a cylinder}$$
$$= (2\pi r)h \qquad P = 2\pi r$$
$$= 2\pi(6)(14) \qquad r = 6,\ h = 14$$
$$\approx 527.8 \qquad \text{Simplify.}$$

Find the area of each base.

$$B = \pi r^2 \qquad \text{Area of a circle}$$
$$= \pi(6)^2 \qquad r = 6$$
$$\approx 113.1 \qquad \text{Simplify.}$$

The total area is the lateral area plus the area of the two bases.
$T = 527.8 + 113.1 + 113.1$ or 754 square centimeters.

Exercises

Find the surface area of each cylinder. Round to the nearest tenth.

1.

2.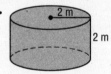

3.

4.

5.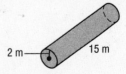

6.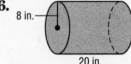

12-3 Skills Practice

Surface Areas of Cylinders

Find the surface area of a cylinder with the given dimensions. Round to the nearest tenth.

1. $r = 10$ in., $h = 12$ in.

2. $r = 8$ cm, $h = 15$ cm

3. $r = 5$ ft, $h = 20$ ft

4. $d = 20$ yd, $h = 5$ yd

5. $d = 8$ m, $h = 7$ m

6. $d = 24$ mm, $h = 20$ mm

Find the surface area of each cylinder. Round to the nearest tenth.

7.

5 ft
7 ft

8.

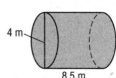

4 m
8.5 m

Find the radius of the base of each cylinder.

9. The surface area is 603.2 square meters, and the height is 10 meters.

10. The surface area is 100.5 square inches, and the height is 6 inches.

11. The surface area is 226.2 square centimeters, and the height is 5 centimeters.

12. The surface area is 1520.5 square yards, and the height is 14.2 yards.

Lesson 12-3

12-3 Practice

Surface Areas of Cylinders

Find the surface area of a cylinder with the given dimensions. Round to the nearest tenth.

1. $r = 8$ cm, $h = 9$ cm

2. $r = 12$ in., $h = 14$ in.

3. $d = 14$ mm, $h = 32$ mm

4. $d = 6$ yd, $h = 12$ yd

5. $r = 2.5$ ft, $h = 7$ ft

6. $d = 13$ m, $h = 20$ m

Find the surface area of each cylinder. Round to the nearest tenth.

7.
19 in.
17 in.

8.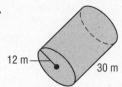
12 m
30 m

Find the radius of the base of each right cylinder.

9. The surface area is 628.3 square millimeters, and the height is 15 millimeters.

10. The surface area is 892.2 square feet, and the height is 4.2 feet.

11. The surface area is 158.3 square inches, and the height is 5.4 inches.

12. KALEIDOSCOPES Nathan built a kaleidoscope with a 20-centimeter barrel and a 5-centimeter diameter. He plans to cover the barrel with embossed paper of his own design. How many square centimeters of paper will it take to cover the barrel of the kaleidoscope?

12-3 Word Problem Practice

Surface Areas of Cylinders

1. DRUMS A drum is shaped like a cylinder with a height of 5 inches and a radius of 7 inches. What is the surface area of the drum? Round your answer to the nearest hundredth.

2. DRINKING GLASSES A drinking glass is shaped like a cylinder with a height of 7 inches and a diameter of 3 inches.

What is the surface area of the drinking glass? Remember that the glass has an open top. Round your answer to the nearest hundredth.

3. ORIGAMI Hank takes a square sheet of paper and rolls it into a cylinder. The square is 10 inches by 10 inches.

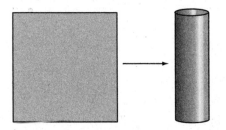

What are the dimensions of the cylinder and what is the lateral area of the cylinder? Round your answers to the nearest hundredth.

4. EXHAUST PIPES An exhaust pipe is shaped like a cylinder with a height of 50 inches and a radius of 2 inches. What is the lateral surface area of the exhaust pipe? Round your answer to the nearest hundredth.

TOWERS For Exercises 5 and 6, use the following information.

A circular tower is made by placing one cylinder on top of another. Both cylinders have a height of 18 inches. The top cylinder has a radius of 18 inches and the bottom cylinder has a radius of 36 inches.

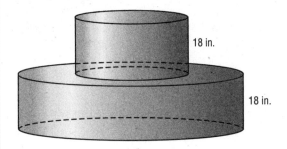

18 in.

18 in.

5. What is the total surface area of the tower? Round your answer to the nearest hundredth.

6. Another tower is constructed by placing the original tower on top of another cylinder with a height of 18 inches and a radius of 54 inches. What is the total surface area of the new tower? Round your answer to the nearest hundredth.

Lesson 12-3

12-3 Enrichment

Minimizing Cost in Manufacturing

Suppose that a manufacturer wants to make a can that has a volume of
40 cubic inches The cost to make the can is 3 cents per square inch for
the top and bottom and 1 cent per square inch for the side.

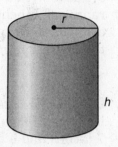

1. Write the value of h in terms of r.

2. Write a formula for the cost in terms of r.

3. Use a graphing calculator to graph the formula, letting Y_1 represent the cost and X
   represent r. Use the graph to estimate the point at which the cost is minimized.

4. Repeat the procedure using 2 cents per square inch for the top and bottom and 4 cents
   per square inch for the top and bottom.

5. What would you expect to happen as the cost of the top and bottom increases?

6. Compute the table for the cost value given. What happens to the height of the can as
   the cost of the top and bottom increases?

Cost Top & Bottom	Cost Cylinder	Minimum h
2 cents	1 cent	
3 cents	1 cent	
4 cents	1 cent	
5 cents	1 cent	
6 cents	1 cent	

12-3 Spreadsheet Activity

Surface Areas of Cylinders

You can use a spreadsheet to determine the surface area of a cylinder.

Example 1 Lucy wants to wrap a Mother's Day gift. The gift she has bought for her mother is in a cylindrical box that is 6 inches tall and has a radius of 3 inches. She must determine the surface area of the box to determine how much wrapping paper to buy. Use a spreadsheet to determine the surface area of the box. Round to the nearest tenth.

Step 1 Use cell A1 for the radius of the cylinder and cell B1 for the height.

Step 2 In cell C1, enter an equals sign followed by 2*PI()*A1*B1+2*PI()*A1^2. Then press ENTER. This will return the surface area of the cylinder.

The surface area of the cylindrical box is 169.6 in^2 to the nearest tenth.

Example 2 Use a spreadsheet to determine the surface area of a cylinder that has a radius of 2.5 centimeters and a height of 5.2 centimeters. Round to the nearest tenth.

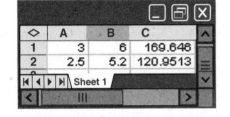

Step 1 Use cell A2 for the radius of the cylinder and cell B2 for the height.

Step 2 Click on the bottom right corner of cell C1 and drag it to C2. This returns the surface area of the cylinder.

The surface area of the cylinder is 121.0 cm^2 to the nearest tenth.

Exercises ...heet to find the surface area of each cylinder with the given dimensions. Round to the nearest tenth.

1. $r = 12$ m, $h = 2.3$ m

2. $r = 6$ m, $h = 2$ m

3. $r = 3$ in., $h = 7$ in.

4. $r = 5$ in., $h = 11$ in.

5. $r = 1$ ft, $h = 3$ ft

6. $r = 3$ ft, $h = 1.5$ ft

7. $r = 10$ mm, $h = 20$ mm

8. $r = 1.5$ mm, $h = 4.5$ mm

9. $r = 6.2$ cm, $h = 1.2$ cm

10. $r = 10$ cm, $h = 15$ cm

11. $r = 10$ m, $h = 2$ m

12. $r = 11$ m, $h = 13$ m

Lesson 12-3

12-4 Lesson Reading Guide

Surface Areas of Pyramids

Get Ready for the Lesson

Read the introduction to Lesson 12-4 in your textbook.

Why do you think that the architect for the new entrance to the Louvre decided to use a pyramid rather than a rectangular prism?

Read the Lesson

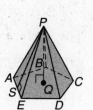

1. In the figure, *ABCDE* has congruent sides and congruent angles.

   a. Describe this pyramid with as specific a name as possible.

   b. Use the figure to name the base of this pyramid.

   c. Describe the base of the pyramid.

   d. Name the vertex of the pyramid.

   e. Name the lateral faces of the pyramid.

   f. Describe the lateral faces.

   g. Name the lateral edges of the pyramid.

   h. Name the altitude of the pyramid.

   i. Write an expression for the height of the pyramid.

   j. Write an expression for the slant height of the pyramid.

2. In a regular square pyramid, let *s* represent the side length of the base, *h* represent the height, *a* represent the apothem, and ℓ represent the slant height. Also, let *L* represent the lateral area and let *T* represent the surface area. Which of the following relationships are correct?

   A. $s = 2a$ **B.** $a^2 + \ell^2 = h^2$ **C.** $L = 4\ell s$

   D. $h = \sqrt{\ell^2 - a^2}$ **E.** $\left(\frac{s}{2}\right)^2 + h^2 = \ell^2$ **F.** $T = s^2 + 2\ell s$

Remember What You Learned

3. A good way to remember something is to explain it to someone else. Suppose that one of your classmates is having trouble remembering the difference between the *height* and the *slant height* of a regular pyramid. How can you explain this concept?

12-4 Study Guide and Intervention

Surface Areas of Pyramids

Lateral Areas of Regular Pyramids Here are some properties of pyramids.
- The base is a polygon.
- All of the faces, except the base, intersect in a common point known as the **vertex**.
- The faces that intersect at the vertex, which are called **lateral faces**, are triangles.

For a **regular pyramid**, the base is a regular polygon and the **slant height** is the height of each lateral face.

Lateral Area of a Regular Pyramid	If a regular pyramid has a lateral area of L square units, a slant height of ℓ units, and its base has a perimeter of P units, then $L = \frac{1}{2}P\ell$.

Example The roof of a barn is a regular octagonal pyramid. The base of the pyramid has sides of 12 feet, and the slant height of the roof is 15 feet. Find the lateral area of the roof.

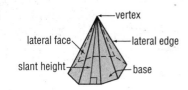

The perimeter of the base is 8(12) or 96 feet.

$L = \frac{1}{2}P\ell$ Lateral area of a pyramid

$= \frac{1}{2}(96)(15)$ $P = 96$, $\ell = 15$

$= 720$ Multiply.

The lateral area is 720 square feet.

Exercises

Find the lateral area of each regular pyramid. Round to the nearest tenth if necessary.

1.
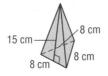

2.
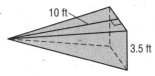

3.

4.
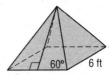

5.
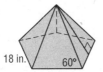

6.

Lesson 12-4

12-4 Study Guide and Intervention *(continued)*

Surface Areas of Pyramids

Surface Areas of Regular Pyramids The surface area of a regular pyramid is the lateral area plus the area of the base.

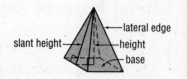

Surface Area of a Regular Pyramid	If a regular pyramid has a surface area of T square units, a slant height of ℓ units, and its base has a perimeter of P units and an area of B square units, then $T = \frac{1}{2}P\ell + B$.

Example For the regular square pyramid above, find the surface area to the nearest tenth if each side of the base is 12 centimeters and the height of the pyramid is 8 centimeters.

Look at the pyramid above. The slant height is the hypotenuse of a right triangle. One leg of that triangle is the height of the pyramid, and the other leg is half the length of a side of the base. Use the Pythagorean Theorem to find the slant height ℓ.

$\ell^2 = 6^2 + 8^2$ Pythagorean Theorem

$\quad = 100$ Simplify.

$\ell = 10$ Take the square root of each side.

$T = \frac{1}{2}P\ell + B$ Surface area of a pyramid

$\quad = \frac{1}{2}(4)(12)(10) + 12^2$ $P = (4)(12)$, $\ell = 10$, $B = 12^2$

$\quad = 384$ Simplify.

The surface area is 384 square centimeters.

Exercises

Find the surface area of each regular pyramid. Round to the nearest tenth if necessary.

1.
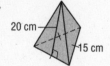

2.
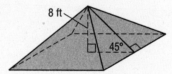

3.
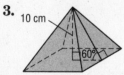

4.

5.
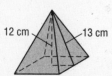

6.

12-4 Skills Practice

Surface Areas of Pyramids

Find the surface area of each regular pyramid. Round to the nearest tenth if necessary.

1.
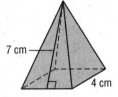
7 cm
4 cm

2.
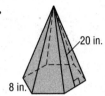
20 in.
8 in.

3.
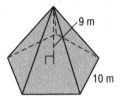
9 m
10 m

4.
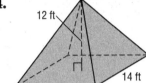
12 ft
14 ft

5.

9 mm
6 mm

6.
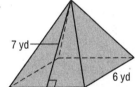
7 yd
6 yd

7.
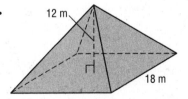
12 m
18 m

8.
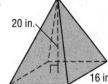
20 in.
16 in.

Lesson 12-4

12-4 Practice

Surface Areas of Pyramids

Find the surface area of each regular pyramid. Round to the nearest tenth if necessary.

1.

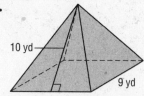

10 yd

9 yd

2.

12 m

7 m

3.

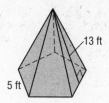

13 ft

5 ft

4.

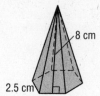

8 cm

2.5 cm

5.

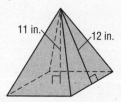

11 in.   12 in.

6.

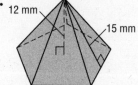

12 mm   15 mm

7.

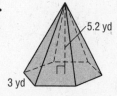

5.2 yd

3 yd

8.

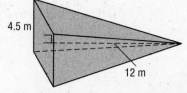

4.5 m

12 m

9. **GAZEBOS** The roof of a gazebo is a regular octagonal pyramid. If the base of the pyramid has sides of 0.5 meters and the slant height of the roof is 1.9 meters, find the area of the roof.

12-4 Word Problem Practice

Surface Areas of Pyramids

1. **PAPER MODELS** Patrick is making a paper model of a castle. Part of the model involves cutting out the net shown and folding it into a
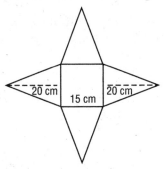
pyramid. The pyramid has a square base. What is the lateral surface area of the resulting pyramid?

2. **TETRAHEDRON** Sung Li builds a paper model of a regular tetrahedron, a pyramid with an equilateral triangle for the base and three equilateral triangles for the lateral faces. One of the faces of the tetrahedron has an area of 17 square inches. What is the total surface area of the tetrahedron?

3. **PAPERWEIGHTS** Daphne uses a paperweight shaped like a pyramid with a regular hexagon for a base. The side length of the regular hexagon is 1 inch. The altitude of the pyramid is 2 inches.

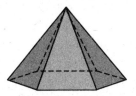

What is the lateral surface area of this pyramid? Round your answers to the nearest hundredth.

4. **DICE** A game needs random numbers between 1 and 8, inclusive. For that reason, the game uses a die in the shape of a regular octahedron. (A regular octahedron can be made by attaching two square pyramids together along their bases.) The lateral faces are congruent equilateral triangles with side length 2 centimeters. What is the surface area of the die?

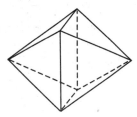

Round your answer to the nearest hundredth.

CHEESE For Exercises 5 and 6, use the following information.

A piece of goat cheese is sold in the shape of a square pyramid. The base has a side length of 4 inches and the altitude is 3 inches. Round your answers to the nearest hundredth.

5. Caroline cuts off the tip of the cheese by slicing the pyramid along a plane parallel to the base resulting in a smaller square pyramid with an altitude of 1 inch. What is the surface area of this cheese tip?

6. What is the surface area of the remaining part of the cheese?

Lesson 12-4

12-4 Enrichment

Two Truncated Solids

To create a truncated solid, you could start with an ordinary solid and then cut off the corners. Another way to make such a shape is to use the patterns on this page.

The Truncated Octahedron

1. Two copies of the pattern at the right can be used to make a *truncated octahedron*, a solid with 6 square faces and 8 regular hexagonal faces.

   Each pattern makes half of the truncated octahedron. Attach adjacent faces using glue or tape to make a cup-shaped figure.

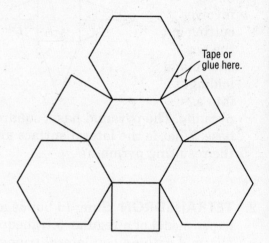

Tape or glue here.

The Truncated Tetrahedron

2. The pattern below will make a *truncated tetrahedron*, a solid with 8 polygonal faces: 4 hexagons and 4 equilateral triangles.

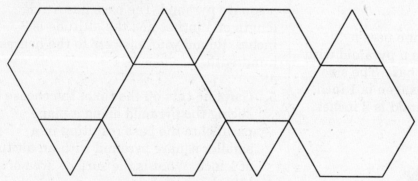

Solve.

3. Find the surface area of the truncated octahedron if each polygon in the pattern has sides of 3 inches.

4. Find the surface area of the truncated tetrahedron if each polygon in the pattern has sides of 3 inches.

Area Formulas for Regular Polygons	
(s is the length of one side)	
triangle	$A = \frac{s^2}{4}\sqrt{3}$
hexagon	$A = \frac{3s^2}{2}\sqrt{3}$
octagon	$A = 2s^2(\sqrt{2} + 1)$

12-5 Lesson Reading Guide

Surface Areas of Cones

Get Ready for the Lesson

Read the introduction to Lesson 12-5 in your textbook.

If you wanted to build a tepee of a certain size, how would it help you to know the formula for the lateral area of a cone?

Read the Lesson

1.

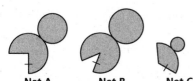

Net A   Net B   Net C

   a. Which net will give the cone with the greatest lateral area?

   b. Which net will give the tallest cone?

2. Refer to the figure at the right. Suppose you have removed the circular base of the cone and cut from V to A so that you can unroll the lateral surface onto a flat table.

   a. How can you be sure that the flattened-out piece is a sector of a circle?

   b. How do you know that the flattened-out piece is not a full circle?

3. Suppose you have a right cone with radius r, diameter d, height h, and slant height ℓ. Which of the following relationships involving these lengths are correct?

   A. $r = 2d$ **B.** $r + h = \ell$ **C.** $r^2 + h^2 = \ell^2$

   D. $r^2 + \ell^2 = h^2$ **E.** $r = \sqrt{\ell^2 - h^2}$ **F.** $h = \pm\sqrt{\ell^2 - r^2}$

Remember What You Learned

4. One way to remember a new formula is to relate it to a formula you already know. Explain how the formulas for the lateral areas of a pyramid and a cone are similar.

Lesson 12-5

12-5 **Study Guide and Intervention** (continued)

Surface Areas of Cones

Lateral Areas of Cones Cones have the following properties.

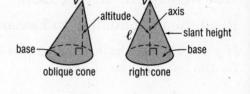

- A cone has one circular base and one vertex.
- The segment whose endpoints are the vertex and the center of the base is the **axis** of the cone.
- The segment that has one endpoint at the vertex, is perpendicular to the base, and has its other endpoint on the base is the **altitude** of the cone.
- For a **right cone** the axis is also the altitude, and any segment from the circumference of the base to the vertex is the **slant height** ℓ. If a cone is not a right cone, it is oblique.

Lateral Area of a Cone	If a cone has a lateral area of L square units, a slant height of ℓ units, and the radius of the base is r units, then $L = \pi r \ell$.

Example Find the lateral area of a cone with slant height of 10 centimeters and a base with a radius of 6 centimeters.

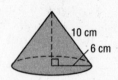

$L = \pi r \ell$ Lateral area of a cone
$ = \pi(6)(10)$ $r = 6, \ell = 10$
$ \approx 188.5$ Simplify.

The lateral area is about 188.5 square centimeters.

Exercises

Find lateral area of each cone. Round to the nearest tenth.

1.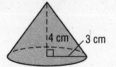

2.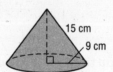

3.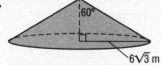

4.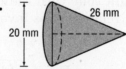

5.

6.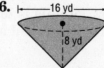

12-5 Study Guide and Intervention *(continued)*
Surface Areas of Cones

Surface Areas of Cones The surface area of a cone is the
lateral area of the cone plus the area of the base.

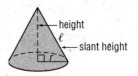

Surface Area of a Right Cone	If a cone has a surface area of *T* square units, a slant height of ℓ units, and the radius of the base is *r* units, then $T = \pi r \ell + \pi r^2$.

Example For the cone above, find the surface area to the nearest tenth if the
radius is 6 centimeters and the height is 8 centimeters.

The slant height is the hypotenuse of a right triangle with legs of length 6 and 8. Use the
Pythagorean Theorem.

$\ell^2 = 6^2 + 8^2$ Pythagorean Theorem
$\ell^2 = 100$ Simplify.
$\ell = 10$ Take the square root of each side.

$T = \pi r \ell + \pi r^2$ Surface area of a cone
    $= \pi(6)(10) + \pi \cdot 6^2$ $r = 6, \ell = 10$
    ≈ 301.6 Simplify.

The surface area is about 301.6 square centimeters.

Exercises

Find the surface area of each cone. Round to the nearest tenth.

1.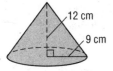
12 cm
9 cm

2.
5 ft
30°

3.
12 cm
13 cm

4.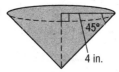
45°
4 in.

5.
26 m
40 m

6.
$8\sqrt{3}$ yd
60°

Lesson 12-5

12-5 **Skills Practice**

Surface Areas of Cones

Find the surface area of each cone. Round to the nearest tenth if necessary.

1.

5 m
14 m

2.
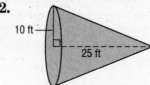
10 ft
25 ft

3.

21 in.
8 in.

4.
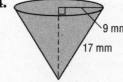
9 mm
17 mm

5.
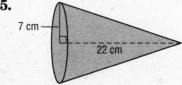
7 cm
22 cm

6.
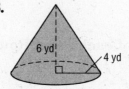
6 yd
4 yd

7. Find the surface area of a cone if the height is 12 inches and the slant height is 15 inches.

8. Find the surface area of a cone if the height is 9 centimeters and the slant height is 12 centimeters.

9. Find the surface area of a cone if the height is 10 meters and the slant height is 14 meters.

10. Find the surface area of a cone if the height is 5 feet and the slant height is 7 feet.

12-5 Practice

Surface Areas of Cones

Find the surface area of each cone. Round to the nearest tenth if necessary.

1.

9 in. — 13 in.

2.

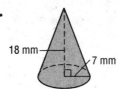

18 mm — 7 mm

3.

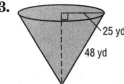

25 yd
48 yd

4.

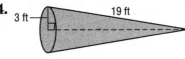

3 ft — 19 ft

5.

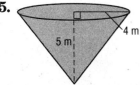

5 m — 4 m

6.

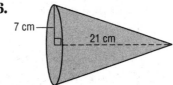

7 cm — 21 cm

7. Find the surface area of a cone if the height is 8 feet and the slant height is 10 feet.

8. Find the surface area of a cone if the height is 14 centimeters and the slant height is 16.4 centimeters.

9. Find the surface area of a cone if the height is 12 inches and the diameter is 27 inches.

10. HATS Cuong bought a conical hat on a recent trip to central Vietnam. The basic frame of the hat is 16 hoops of bamboo that gradually diminish in size. The hat is covered in palm leaves. If the hat has a diameter of 50 centimeters and a slant height of 32 centimeters, what is the lateral area of the conical hat?

Lesson 12-5

12-5 **Word Problem Practice**

Surface Areas of Cones

1. HALF CIRCLES Charles cuts out a semicircle with a radius of 5 inches from a piece of paper. He then curls it into a cone by joining the two radii on the edge of the semicircle together.

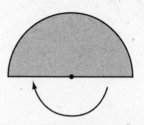

What is the lateral surface area of the resulting cone? Round your answer to the nearest hundredth.

2. CASTLES A right circular cone with an altitude of 20 feet and a radius of 6 feet serves as the highest cap of a castle.

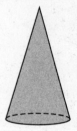

What is the lateral surface area of this cone? Round your answer to the nearest hundredth.

3. PAINTING Naomi is asked to paint a number of congruent cones. She is told that the radius of the cones is 6 inches and the altitude of the cones is 2 inches. What is the surface area of one of the cones? Round your answer to the nearest hundredth.

4. SPRAY PAINT A can of spray paint shoots out paint in a cone shaped mist. The lateral surface area of the cone is 65π square inches when the can is held 12 inches from a canvas. What is the area of the part of the canvas that gets sprayed with paint? Round your answer to the nearest hundredth.

MEGAPHONES For Exercises 5-7, use the following information.

A megaphone is formed by taking a cone with a radius of 20 centimeters and an altitude of 60 centimeters and cutting off the tip. The cut is made along a plane that is perpendicular to the axis of the cone and intersects the axis 12 centimeters from the vertex. Round your answer to the nearest hundredth.

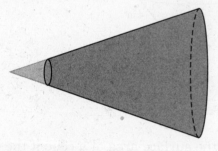

5. What is the lateral surface area of the original cone?

6. What is the lateral surface area of the tip that is removed?

7. What is the lateral surface area of the megaphone?

12-5 Enrichment

Cone Patterns

**The pattern at the right is made from a
circle. It can be folded to make a cone.**

1. Measure the radius of the circle to the
   nearest centimeter.

2. The pattern is what fraction of the
   complete circle?

3. What is the circumference of the complete
   circle?

4. How long is the circular arc that is the
   outside of the pattern?

5. Cut out the pattern and tape it together to
   form a cone.

6. Measure the diameter of the circular base of the cone.

7. What is the circumference of the base of the cone?

8. What is the slant height of the cone?

9. Use the Pythagorean Theorem to calculate the height of the cone.
   Use a decimal approximation. Check your calculation by measuring
   the height with a metric ruler.

10. Find the lateral area.

11. Find the total surface area.

**Make a paper pattern for each cone with the given measurements.
Then cut the pattern out and make the cone. Find the measurements.**

12.

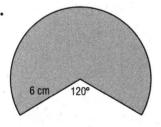

6 cm   120°

    diameter of base =

    lateral area =

    height of cone =
    (to nearest tenth of a centimeter)

13.

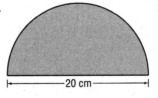

|———20 cm———|

    diameter of base =

    lateral area =

    height of cone =
    (to nearest tenth of a centimeter)

Lesson 12-5

12-6 Lesson Reading Guide

Surface Areas of Spheres

Get Ready for the Lesson

Read the introduction to Lesson 12-6 in your textbook.

How would knowing the formula for the surface area of a sphere help make the world's largest soccer ball?

_____

Read the Lesson

1. In the figure, P is the center of the sphere. Name each of the following in the figure.

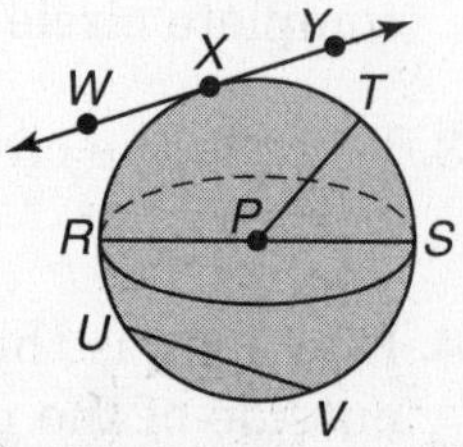

   a. three radii of the sphere

   b. a diameter of the sphere

   c. two chords of the sphere

   d. a great circle of the sphere

   e. a tangent to the sphere

   f. the point of tangency

2. Determine whether each sentence is *sometimes*, *always*, or *never* true.

   a. If a sphere and a plane intersect in more than one point, their intersection will be a great circle.

   b. A great circle has the same center as the sphere.

   c. The endpoints of a radius of a sphere are two points on the sphere.

   d. A chord of a sphere is a diameter of the sphere.

   e. A radius of a great circle is also a radius of the sphere.

3. Match each surface area formula with the name of the appropriate solid.

   a. $T = \pi r \ell + \pi r^2$ **i.** regular pyramid

   b. $T = Ph + 2B$ **ii.** hemisphere

   c. $T = 4\pi r^2$ **iii.** cylinder

   d. $T = \frac{1}{2}P\ell + B$ **iv.** prism

   e. $T = 2\pi rh + 2\pi r^2$ **v.** sphere

   f. $T = 3\pi r^2$ **vi.** cone

Remember What You Learned

4. Many students have trouble remembering all of the formulas they have learned in this chapter. What is an easy way to remember the formula for the surface area of a sphere?

12-6 Study Guide and Intervention

Surface Areas of Spheres

Properties of Spheres A **sphere** is the locus of all points that are a given distance from a given point called its **center**.

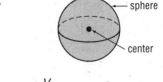

Here are some terms associated with a sphere.

- A **radius** is a segment whose endpoints are the center of the sphere and a point on the sphere.
- A **chord** is a segment whose endpoints are points on the sphere.
- A **diameter** is a chord that contains the sphere's center.
- A **tangent** is a line that intersects the sphere in exactly one point.
- A **great circle** is the intersection of a sphere and a plane that contains the center of the sphere.
- A **hemisphere** is one-half of a sphere. Each great circle of a sphere determines two hemispheres.

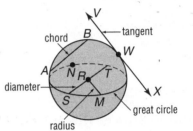

$\overline{RS}$ is a radius. $\overline{AB}$ is a chord.
$\overline{ST}$ is a diameter. $\overrightarrow{VX}$ is a tangent.
The circle that contains points S, M, T, and N is a great circle; it determines two hemispheres.

Example Determine the shapes you get when you intersect a plane with a sphere.

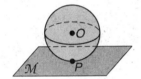

The intersection of plane $\mathcal{M}$ and sphere O is point P.

The intersection of plane $\mathcal{N}$ and sphere O is circle Q.

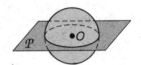

The intersection of plane $\mathcal{P}$ and sphere O is circle O.

A plane can intersect a sphere in a point, in a circle, or in a great circle.

Exercises

Describe each object as a model of a *circle*, a *sphere*, a *hemisphere*, or *none of these*.

1. a baseball

2. a pancake

3. the Earth

4. a kettle grill cover

5. a basketball rim

6. cola can

Determine whether each statement is *true* or *false*.

7. All lines intersecting a sphere are tangent to the sphere.

8. Every plane that intersects a sphere makes a great circle.

9. The eastern hemisphere of Earth is congruent to the western hemisphere.

10. The diameter of a sphere is congruent to the diameter of a great circle.

12-6 Study Guide and Intervention (continued)

Surface Areas of Spheres

Surface Areas of Spheres You can think of the surface area of a sphere as the total area of all of the nonoverlapping strips it would take to cover the sphere. If r is the radius of the sphere, then the area of a great circle of the sphere is πr^2. The total surface area of the sphere is four times the area of a great circle.

Surface Area of a Sphere	If a sphere has a surface area of T square units and a radius of r units, then $T = 4\pi r^2$.

Example Find the surface area of a sphere to the nearest tenth if the radius of the sphere is 6 centimeters.

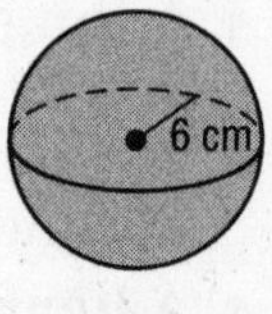

$T = 4\pi r^2$ Surface area of a sphere
$\quad = 4\pi \cdot 6^2$ $r = 6$
$\quad \approx 452.4$ Simplify.

The surface area is 452.4 square centimeters.

Exercises

Find the surface area of each sphere with the given radius or diameter to the nearest tenth.

1. $r = 8$ cm

2. $r = 2\sqrt{2}$ ft

3. $r = \pi$ cm

4. $d = 10$ in.

5. $d = 6\pi$ m

6. $d = 16$ yd

7. Find the surface area of a hemisphere with radius 12 centimeters.

8. Find the surface area of a hemisphere with diameter π centimeters.

9. Find the radius of a sphere if the surface area of a hemisphere is 192π square centimeters.

12-6 Skills Practice

Surface Areas of Spheres

In the figure, A is the center of the sphere, and plane T intersects the sphere in circle E. Round to the nearest tenth if necessary.

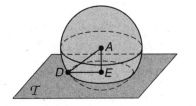

1. If $AE = 5$ and $DE = 12$, find AD.

2. If $AE = 7$ and $DE = 15$, find AD.

3. If the radius of the sphere is 18 units and the radius of $\odot E$ is 17 units, find AE.

4. If the radius of the sphere is 10 units and the radius of $\odot E$ is 9 units, find AE.

5. If M is a point on $\odot E$ and $AD = 23$, find AM.

Find the surface area of each sphere or hemisphere. Round to the nearest tenth.

6.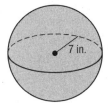

7.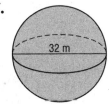

8. a hemisphere with a radius of the great circle 8 yards

9. a hemisphere with a radius of the great circle 2.5 millimeters

10. a sphere with the area of a great circle 28.6 inches

12-6 Practice

Surface Areas of Spheres

In the figure, C is the center of the sphere, and plane $\mathcal{B}$ intersects the sphere in circle R. Round to the nearest tenth if necessary.

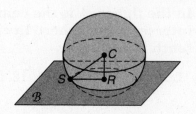

1. If $CR = 4$ and $SR = 14$, find CS.

2. If $CR = 7$ and $SR = 24$, find CS.

3. If the radius of the sphere is 28 units and the radius of $\odot R$ is 26 units, find CR.

4. If J is a point on $\odot R$ and $CS = 7.3$, find CJ.

Find the surface area of each sphere or hemisphere. Round to the nearest tenth.

5.

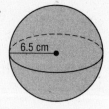

6.

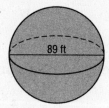

7. a sphere with the area of a great circle 29.8 meters

8. a hemisphere with a radius of the great circle 8.4 inches

9. a hemisphere with the circumference of a great circle 18 millimeters

10. **SPORTS** A standard size 5 soccer ball for ages 13 and older has a circumference of 27–28 inches. Suppose Breck is on a team that plays with a 28-inch soccer ball. Find the surface area of the ball.

12-6 Word Problem Practice

Surface Areas of Spheres

1. **ORANGES** Mandy cuts a spherical orange in half along a great circle. If the radius of the orange is 2 inches, what is the area of the cross section that Mandy cut? Round your answer to the nearest hundredth.

2. **COFFEE TABLES** A coffee table is made by taking a sphere with a radius of 26 inches and then cutting it along two parallel planes. The two planes are both 10 inches from the center of the sphere. The section of the sphere that contains its center is used as the table.

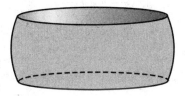

What is the area of the tabletop?

3. **MOONS OF SATURN** The planet Saturn has several moons. These can be modeled accurately by spheres. Saturn's largest moon Titan has a radius of about 2575 kilometers. What is the approximate surface area of Titan? Round your answer to the nearest tenth.

4. **METEORS** A spherical meteorite lies half exposed in the earth. The diameter of the meteorite is 14 inches. What is the surface area of the exposed surface? Round your answer to the nearest hundredth.

CUBES For Exercises 5-7, use the following information.

Marcus builds a spherical container for a cube. The cube fits snugly inside the sphere so that the vertices of the cube touch the inside of the sphere. The side length of the cube is 2 inches.

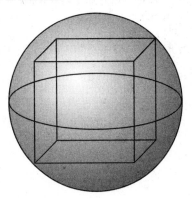

5. What is the surface area of the cube?

6. What is the surface area of the sphere? Round your answers to the nearest hundredth.

7. What is the ratio of the surface area of the cube to the surface area of the sphere? Round your answer to the nearest hundredth.

12-6 Enrichment

Doubling Sizes

Consider what happens to surface area when the sides of a figure are doubled.

The sides of the large cube are twice the size of the sides of the small cube.

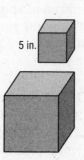

5 in.

1. How long are the edges of the large cube?

2. What is the surface area of the small cube?

3. What is the surface area of the large cube?

4. The surface area of the large cube is how many times greater than that of the small cube?

The radius of the large sphere at the right is twice the radius of the small sphere.

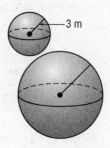

3 m

5. What is the surface area of the small sphere?

6. What is the surface area of the large sphere?

7. The surface area of the large sphere is how many times greater than the surface area of the small sphere?

8. It appears that if the dimensions of a solid are doubled, the surface area is multiplied by _____.

Now consider how doubling the dimensions affects the volume of a cube.

The sides of the large cube are twice the size of the sides of the small cube.

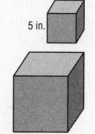

5 in.

9. How long are the edges of the large cube?

10. What is the volume of the small cube?

11. What is the volume of the large cube?

12. The volume of the large cube is how many times greater than that of the small cube?

The large sphere at the right has twice the radius of the small sphere.

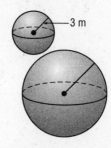

3 m

13. What is the volume of the small sphere?

14. What is the volume of the large sphere?

15. The volume of the large sphere is how many times greater than the volume of the small sphere?

16. It appears that if the dimensions of a solid are doubled, the volume is multiplied by _____.

12 Student Recording Sheet

Read each question. Then fill in the correct answer.

1. (A) (B) (C) (D)

2. (F) (G) (H) (J)

3. Record your answer and fill in the bubbles in the grid below. Be sure to use the correct place value.

				.			
(0)	(0)	(0)	(0)		(0)	(0)	(0)
(1)	(1)	(1)	(1)		(1)	(1)	(1)
(2)	(2)	(2)	(2)		(2)	(2)	(2)
(3)	(3)	(3)	(3)		(3)	(3)	(3)
(4)	(4)	(4)	(4)		(4)	(4)	(4)
(5)	(5)	(5)	(5)		(5)	(5)	(5)
(6)	(6)	(6)	(6)		(6)	(6)	(6)
(7)	(7)	(7)	(7)		(7)	(7)	(7)
(8)	(8)	(8)	(8)		(8)	(8)	(8)
(9)	(9)	(9)	(9)		(9)	(9)	(9)

4. (A) (B) (C) (D)

5. (F) (G) (H) (J)

6. (A) (B) (C) (D)

7. (F) (G) (H) (J)

8. (A) (B) (C) (D)

9. (F) (G) (H) (J)

Pre-AP

Record your answers for Question 10 on the back of this paper.

Assessment

12   Rubric for Scoring Pre-AP

General Scoring Guidelines

- If a student gives only a correct numerical answer to a problem but does not show how he or she arrived at the answer, the student will be awarded only 1 credit. All extended response questions require the student to show work.

- A fully correct answer for a multiple-part question requires correct responses for all parts of the question. For example, if a question has three parts, the correct response to one or two parts of the question that required work to be shown is *not* considered a fully correct response.

- Students who use trial and error to solve a problem must show their method. Merely showing that the answer checks or is correct is not considered a complete response for full credit.

Exercise 13 Rubric

Score	Specific Criteria
4	A correct solution that is supported by well-developed, accurate explanations. The surface area of the cone is $((\pi \cdot 4 \cdot 7) + (\pi \cdot 4^2)) = 138$ in^2. The surface area of the cylinder is $((2 \cdot \pi \cdot 4 \cdot 22) + (2 \cdot \pi 4^2)) = 653$ in^2. The surface area of the rocket once assembled is $(138 + 653) = 691$ in^2.
3	A generally correct solution, but may contain minor flaws in reasoning or computation.
2	A partially correct interpretation and/or solution to the problem.
1	A correct solution with no supporting evidence or explanation.
0	An incorrect solution indicating no mathematical understanding of the concept or task, or no solution is given.

12 Chapter 12 Quiz 1

SCORE _____

(Lessons 12–1 and 12–2)

1. Given the corner view of a figure, draw the left view.

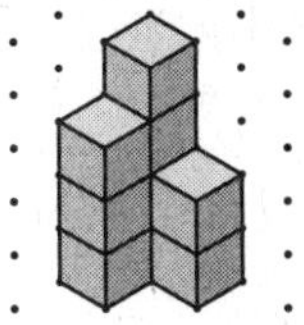

1. _____

2. Sketch a rectangular prism.

2. _____

3. Find the lateral area of the hexagonal prism.

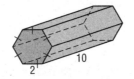

3. _____

4. Find the surface area of a rectangular prism with a length and width of 6 cm and a height of 12 cm.

4. _____

5. Multiple Choice. Find the surface area of the prism to the nearest hundredth.

   A. 30.5   B. 54   C. 49.45   D. 52.44

5. _____

- -

NAME _____ DATE_____ PERIOD _____

12 Chapter 12 Quiz 2

SCORE _____

(Lesson 12–3)

1. Find the surface area of a right cylinder with a diameter of 4 cm and a height of 6 cm. Round to the nearest hundredth.

1. _____

2. The surface area of a right cylinder with a height of 15 cm is 648π cm^2. Find the diameter.

2. _____

3. Describe the shape of a net that could be used to calculate the lateral area of a cylinder.

3. _____

For Questions 4 and 5, refer to the solid figure. Round to the nearest tenth.

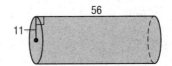

4. Find the lateral area.

4. _____

5. Find the surface area.

5. _____

12 Chapter 12 Quiz 3

(Lessons 12–4 and 12–5)

**For Questions 1 and 2, use the solid figure.
Round to the nearest tenth if necessary.**

1. Find the lateral area.

1. _____

2. Find the surface area to the nearest tenth.

2. _____

3. The lateral area of a pyramid is 200 square centimeters and the base is a rectangle with a length measuring 15 centimeters and a width measuring 4 centimeters. Find the surface area of the pyramid.

3. _____

For Questions 4 and 5, use a right circular cone with a radius of 5 feet and a slant height of 12 feet. Round to the nearest tenth.

4. Find the lateral area.

4. _____

5. Find the surface area.

5. _____

---

12 Chapter 12 Quiz 4

(Lesson 12–6)

For Questions 1–3, refer to the figure.

1. Name a chord of sphere D that is not a diameter.

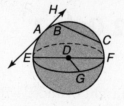

1. _____

2. Name a tangent to the sphere.

2. _____

3. Name a great circle.

3. _____

4. A sphere has a radius that is 18 inches long. Find the surface area of the sphere. Round to the nearest tenth.

4. _____

5. The radius of a sphere is doubled. How is the surface area changed?

5. _____

12 **Chapter 12 Mid-Chapter Test**

SCORE _____

(Lessons 12–1 through 12–6)

Part I *Write the letter for the correct answer in the blank at the right of each question.*

1. Which of the following is a defining feature of a prism?

   A. All faces have equal surface area

   B. Bases are quadrilateral and congruent

   C. Bases are congruent

   D. Lateral edges are also the altitudes

1. _____

2. Which of the following describes a tetrahedron?

   F. triangular pyramid   **H.** square pyramid

   G. triangular prism   **J.** cone

2. _____

3. The surface area of a prism is 120 square centimeters and the area of each base is 32 square centimeters. Find the lateral area of the prism.

   A. 184 cm^2 **B.** 152 cm^2 **C.** 86 cm^2 **D.** 56 cm^2

3. _____

For Questions 4 and 5, refer to the solid figure. Round to the nearest tenth.

4. Find the lateral area.

   F. 9289.1 ft^2 **H.** 10,965.4 ft^2

   G. 9434.2 ft^2 **J.** 12,641.8 ft^2

4. _____

5. Find the surface area.

   A. 9289.1 ft^2 **B.** 9434.2 ft^2 **C.** 10,965.4 ft^2 **D.** 12,641.8 ft^2

5. _____

Part II

6. Draw the top view of the pyramid.

6. _____

7. Draw the net of a right cylinder with a radius of 2 cm and a height of 5 cm.

7. _____

8. A barrel in the shape of a right cylinder has a diameter of 18 inches and a height of 42 inches. Find the surface area of the barrel.

8. _____

9. Find the surface area of the regular hexagonal prism. Round to the nearest tenth.

9. _____

10. Find the total surface area of the solid. Round to the nearest tenth.

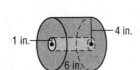

10. _____

Assessment

12 Chapter 12 Vocabulary Test

axis	lateral area	right cylinder
circular cone	lateral edges	right prism
corner view	lateral faces	reflection symmetry
cross section	oblique cone	regular pyramid
great circle	perspective view	slant height
hemisphere	right cone	

Choose from the terms above to complete each sentence.

1. The height of each lateral face of a regular pyramid is called a(n) ___?___ .

1. _____

2. The view of a solid figure from the corner is called a corner view or ___?___ .

2. _____

3. If the axis of a cylinder is also the altitude, then the cylinder is called a(n) ___?___ .

3. _____

4. A great circle separates a sphere into two congruent halves, each called a(n) ___?___ .

4. _____

Chose the correct term to complete each sentence.

5. The segment whose endpoints are the centers of the circular bases of a cylinder is the (*axis* or *hemisphere*).

5. _____

6. When a plane intersects with a sphere so that it contains the center of a sphere, the intersection is called a (*great circle* or *hemisphere*).

6. _____

State whether each sentence is *true* or *false*. If false, replace the underlined word or phrase to make a true sentence.

7. A polyhedron that has all but one face intersecting at one point is a *prism*.

7. _____

8. A *cross section* is the intersection of a plane and a solid figure.

8. _____

9. A hexagonal prism has six *lateral faces*.

9. _____

10. A cone with an axis that is not an altitude is a *right cone*.

10. _____

Define each term in your own words.

11. lateral area

11. _____

12. right prism

12. _____

12 Chapter 12 Test, Form 1

SCORE _____

Assessment

Write the letter for the correct answer in the blank at the right of each question.

1. Which of these is part of an orthographic drawing?   1. _____
   A. a perspective view   **C.** a two-dimensional top view
   B. a corner view   **D.** a three-dimensional view

For Questions 2–4, refer to the figure.

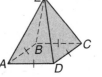

2. Identify this solid figure.   2. _____
   F. square pyramid   **H.** triangular pyramid
   G. square prism   **J.** triangular prism

3. Name the base.   3. _____
   A. △ABE   **B.** □ABCD   **C.** △CDE   **D.** E

4. How many edges does this figure have?   4. _____
   F. 3   **G.** 4   **H.** 6   **J.** 8

5. This net could be folded into a ___?___.   5. _____
   A. tetrahedron
   B. square pyramid
   C. square prism
   D. triangular prism

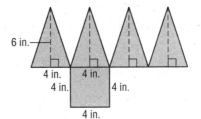

6. Find the surface area of the cube.   6. _____
   F. 9 in^2 **H.** 36 in^2
   G. 27 in^2 **J.** 54 in^2

7. The areas of how many faces of a rectangular prism would be included in the   7. _____
   lateral area?
   A. 2   **B.** 4   **C.** 6   **D.** 8

8. Find the surface area of a rectangular prism with a length of 8 inches, a   8. _____
   width of 5 inches, and a height of 2 inches.
   F. 15 in^2 **G.** 66 in^2 **H.** 80 in^2 **J.** 132 in^2

9. The area of each face of a cube is 60 square centimeters. Find the surface   9. _____
   area of the cube.
   A. 120 cm^2 **B.** 240 cm^2 **C.** 360 cm^2 **D.** 3600 cm^2

10. A cylindrical flower pot with an open top needs to be painted. The height of   10. _____
    the pot is 9 inches and the radius is 3 inches. If it takes Troy 5 minutes to
    paint 40 square inches, how long to the minute will it take him to paint the
    outside of the flower pot?
    F. 20 minutes   **G.** 25 minutes   **H.** 30 minutes   **J.** 35 minutes

12 **Chapter 12 Test, Form 1** *(continued)*

For Questions 11 and 12, refer to the figure.

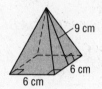

11. Find the lateral area. Round to the nearest tenth.

    A. 75.4 ft²   **C.** 50.3 ft²

    B. 62.8 ft²   **D.** 25.1 ft²

    11. _____

12. Find the surface area. Round to the nearest tenth.

    F. 75.4 ft²   **G.** 62.8 ft²   **H.** 50.3 ft²   **J.** 25.1 ft²

    12. _____

13. The lateral area of a regular pyramid is 300 square units. The perimeter of its base is 100 units. Find the slant height of the pyramid.

    A. 3 units   **B.** 6 units   **C.** 12 units   **D.** 30 units

    13. _____

For Questions 14 and 15, refer to the figure.

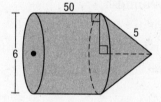

14. Find the lateral area.

    F. 108 cm²   **H.** 162 cm²

    G. 144 cm²   **J.** 324 cm²

    14. _____

15. Find the surface area.

    A. 108 cm²   **B.** 144 cm²   **C.** 162 cm²   **D.** 324 cm²

    15. _____

16. Find the surface area to the nearest tenth.

    F. 546.6 units²   **H.** 1017.9 units²

    G. 989.6 units²   **J.** 1046.2 units²

    16. _____

17. The radius of a right circular cone is 6 inches and the height is 8 inches. Find the slant height of the cone.

    A. 2 in.   **B.** 4 in.   **C.** 10 in.   **D.** 14 in.

    17. _____

18. The radius of a cone is 17 inches long and the slant height is 20 inches. Find the surface area to the nearest tenth.

    F. 18,158.4 in²   **G.** 1976.1 in²   **H.** 1068.1 in²   **J.** 340 in²

    18. _____

19. Which could be the intersection of a sphere and a plane?

    A. line   **B.** square   **C.** oval   **D.** point

    19. _____

20. The diameter of a sphere is 42 centimeters. Find the surface area to the nearest tenth.

    F. 5541.8 cm²   **G.** 2770.9 cm²   **H.** 2167.1 cm²   **J.** 527.8 cm²

    20. _____

Bonus Find the amount of glass needed to cover the sides of the greenhouse shown. The bottom, front, and back are not glass.

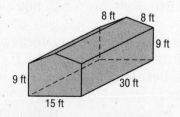

B: _____

12 **Chapter 12 Test, Form 2A**   SCORE _____

Write the letter for the correct answer in the blank at the right of each question.

1. What do the dark segments represent in an orthographic drawing?   1. _____
   A. changes in color   C. designs on the surface
   B. where paper should be folded   D. breaks in the surface

For Questions 2 and 3, refer to the figure.

2. Identify the figure.   2. _____
   F. pyramid   H. cone
   G. prism   J. cylinder

3. Name the base.   3. _____
   A. X B. Y C. $\overline{XY}$ D. $\odot Y$

4. What name is given to a prism that has five faces?   4. _____
   F. pentagonal prism   H. triangular prism
   G. square prism   J. none of these

5. This net could be folded into a ___?___.   5. _____
   A. cone   C. sphere
   B. cylinder   D. triangular prism

6. Find the surface area of the prism.   6. _____
   F. 188 ft^2 H. 288 ft^2
   G. 240 ft^2 J. 480 ft^2
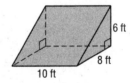

7. The lateral area of a cube is 36 square inches. How long is each edge?   7. _____
   A. $\sqrt{6}$ in.   B. 3 in.   C. 6 in.   D. 9 in.

8. The lateral area of a prism is 56 square inches and the area of each base is   8. _____
   17 square inches. Find the surface area of the prism.
   F. 952 in^2 G. 90 in^2 H. 73 in^2 J. 22 in^2

9. Find the surface area of the outside of the open box.   9. _____
   A. 1920 in^2 C. 752 in^2
   B. 998 in^2 D. 400 in^2
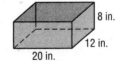

10. The surface area of a right cylinder is 200π square centimeters and the   10. _____
    radius is 4 centimeters. Find the height of the cylinder.
    F. 42 cm   G. 25 cm   H. 23 cm   J. 21 cm

Assessment

For Questions 11 and 12, use a right cylinder with a radius of 3 inches and a height of 17 inches. Round to the nearest tenth.

11. Find the lateral area.   11. _____
    A. 320.4 in²   **B.** 348.7 in²   **C.** 377.0 in²   **D.** 537.2 in²

12. Find the surface area.   12. _____
    F. 320.4 in²   **G.** 348.7 in²   **H.** 377.0 in²   **J.** 537.2 in²

13. The Great Pyramid in Egypt has a square base with each side measuring 230   13. _____
    meters. The lateral height of the pyramid is 146.5 meters. Find the lateral
    surface area of the pyramid.
    A. 67390 m²   **B.** 101085 m²   **C.** 120290 m²   **D.** 134780 m²

For Questions 14 and 15, refer to the figure.

14. Find the lateral area.   14. _____
    F. 144 cm²   **H.** 196 cm²
    G. $144 + 24\sqrt{3}$ cm²   **J.** 288 cm²

15. Find the surface area.   15. _____
    A. 144 cm²   **B.** $144 + 24\sqrt{3}$ cm²   **C.** 196 cm²   **D.** 288 cm²

For Questions 16 and 17, refer to the figure.
Round to the nearest tenth.

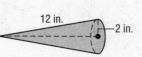

16. Find the lateral area.   16. _____
    F. 44.0 in²   **G.** 75.4 in²   **H.** 88.0 in²   **J.** 100.5 in²

17. Find the surface area.   17. _____
    A. 44.0 in²   **B.** 75.4 in²   **C.** 88.0 in²   **D.** 100.5 in²

18. Find the surface area of this model rocket   18. _____
    to the nearest tenth.
    F. 2890.3 cm²   **H.** 2513.3 cm²
    G. 2576.1 cm²   **J.** 2261.9 cm²

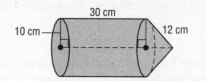

For Questions 19 and 20, refer to the figure.

19. Identify a chord.   19. _____
    A. $\overline{EF}$ **B.** $\odot B$ **C.** $\overline{BD}$ **D.** $\overarc{AD}$

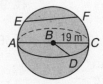

20. Find the surface area to the nearest tenth.   20. _____
    F. 4536.5 m²   **G.** 2268.2 m²   **H.** 477.5 m²   **J.** 238.8 m²

Bonus Find the surface area of the figure   **B:** _____
       to the nearest tenth.

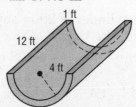

12 Chapter 12 Test, Form 2B

Assessment

Write the letter for the correct answer in the blank at the right of each question.

1. Given the corner view of a figure, which is the top view?

   A. ☐   **B.**   **C.**   **D.**

   1. _____

For Questions 2 and 3, refer to the figure.

2. Identify the figure.
   - **F.** pyramid
   - **G.** prism
   - **H.** cone
   - **J.** cylinder

   2. _____

3. Name a base.
   - **A.** ⊙M
   - **B.** N
   - **C.** $\overline{MN}$
   - **D.** M

   3. _____

4. What name is given to a pyramid that has seven faces?
   - **F.** heptagonal pyramid
   - **G.** hexagonal pyramid
   - **H.** pentagonal pyramid
   - **J.** octagonal pyramid

   4. _____

5. This net could be folded into a ___?___.
   - **A.** rectangular pyramid
   - **B.** rectangular prism
   - **C.** triangular pyramid
   - **D.** triangular prism

   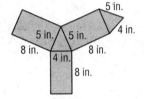

   5. _____

6. Find the surface area of the solid.
   - **F.** 88 cm^2
   - **G.** 102 cm^2
   - **H.** 156 cm^2
   - **J.** 160 cm^2

   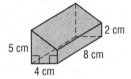

   6. _____

7. Find the lateral area of an equilateral triangular prism if the area of each lateral face is 10 square centimeters.
   - **A.** $10\sqrt{3}$ cm^2
   - **B.** 30 cm^2
   - **C.** 50 cm^2
   - **D.** 100 cm^2

   7. _____

8. The surface area of a cube is 96 square inches. Find the length of an edge.
   - **F.** $\sqrt{24}$ in.
   - **G.** 4 in.
   - **H.** 8 in.
   - **J.** 16 in.

   8. _____

9. The surface area of a rectangular prism is 190 square inches, the length is 10 inches, and the width 3 inches. Find the height.
   - **A.** 30 in.
   - **B.** 20 in.
   - **C.** 10 in.
   - **D.** 5 in.

   9. _____

10. A right cylinder has a radius of 2 feet and a height of 5 feet. Find the surface area of the cylinder.
    - **F.** 20π ft^2
    - **G.** 28π ft^2
    - **H.** 36π ft^2
    - **J.** 40π ft^2

    10. _____

For Questions 11 and 12, use a right cylinder with a radius of 5 centimeters and a height of 22 centimeters. Round to the nearest tenth.

11. Find the lateral area.

   A. 848.2 cm²   **B.** 769.7 cm²   **C.** 691.2 cm²   **D.** 345.6 cm²

11. _____

12. Find the surface area.

   F. 848.2 cm²   **G.** 769.7 cm²   **H.** 691.2 cm²   **J.** 345.6 cm²

12. _____

13. The Third Pyramid has a square base with each side measuring 105.5 meters. The slant height of the pyramid is 65.5 meters. Find the lateral surface area of the pyramid.

   A. 13,820.5 m²   **B.** 20,730.75 m²   **C.** 24,940.75 m²   **D.** 27,641 m²

13. _____

For Questions 14 and 15, use a tetrahedron that has edges of length 12 centimeters.

14. Find the lateral area.

   F. $48\sqrt{3}$ cm²   **G.** $96\sqrt{3}$ cm²   **H.** $108\sqrt{3}$ cm²   **J.** $144\sqrt{3}$ cm²

14. _____

15. Find the surface area.

   A. $48\sqrt{3}$ cm²   **B.** $96\sqrt{3}$ cm²   **C.** $108\sqrt{3}$ cm²   **D.** $144\sqrt{3}$ cm²

15. _____

For Questions 16 and 17, refer to the figure. Round to the nearest tenth.

16. Find the lateral area.

   F. 75.4 cm²   **H.** 131.9 cm²

   G. 103.7 cm²   **J.** 150.8 cm²

16. _____

17. Find the surface area.

   A. 75.4 cm²   **B.** 103.7 cm²   **C.** 131.9 cm²   **D.** 150.8 cm²

17. _____

18. Find the surface area of the solid to the nearest tenth.

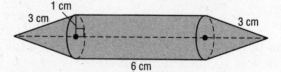

   F. 62.8 cm²   **H.** 47.1 cm²

   G. 56.5 cm²   **J.** 37.7 cm²

18. _____

19. Name a tangent to the sphere.

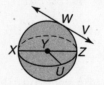

   A. $\overline{YU}$ **C.** $\overset{\frown}{UZ}$

   B. $\overline{XZ}$ **D.** $\overrightarrow{WV}$

19. _____

20. The surface area of a sphere is 64π square centimeters. Find the radius.

   F. 16 cm   **G.** 8 cm   **H.** 4 cm   **J.** 2 cm

20. _____

Bonus Find the surface area of the frustum of a square pyramid.

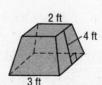

B: _____

12 Chapter 12 Test, Form 2C

1. Given the corner view of a figure, sketch the front view.

1. _____

2. Name the faces of the solid.

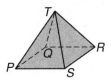

2. _____

3. Identify the solid.

3. _____

4. How many faces does a dodecahedron have?

4. _____

5. Draw a net for the solid.

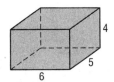

5. _____

6. Find the surface area of the solid.

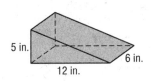

6. _____

7. Find the lateral area of a triangular prism with a height of 8 centimeters, and with bases having sides that measure 4 centimeters, 5 centimeters, and 6 centimeters.

7. _____

8. Find the surface area of the prism.

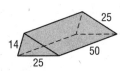

8. _____

9. Find the surface area of the solid. Round to the nearest tenth.

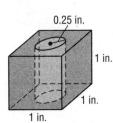

9. _____

10. A gallon of paint costs $12.99 and covers 400 square feet. How many gallons are needed to paint two coats on the walls and ceiling (not the floor) of a rectangular room that is 30 feet long, 18 feet wide, and 8 feet high? Round to the next whole gallon.

10. _____

11. Find the lateral area of a right cylinder with a diameter of
8.6 yards and a height of 19.4 yards. Round to the nearest tenth.

11._____

12. The surface area of a cylinder is 180π square inches and the
height is 9 inches. Find the radius.

12._____

**For Questions 13 and 14, use a regular hexagonal pyramid
with base edges of 10 inches and a slant height of 9 inches.**

13. Find the lateral area.

13._____

14. Find the surface area.

14._____

15. Find the lateral area of the
triangular pyramid.

15._____

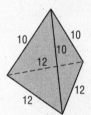

16. The surface area of a regular pyramid is 276 square centimeters,
the slant height measures 8 centimeters, and the area of the
base is 50 square centimeters. Find the perimeter of the base.

16._____

**For Questions 17 and 18, use a right circular cone with a
radius of 4 feet and a height of 3 feet. Round to the nearest
tenth.**

17. Find the lateral area.

17._____

18. Find the surface area.

18._____

19. Plane $\mathcal{A}$ intersects sphere R in $\odot X$.
Find the radius of the sphere.

19._____

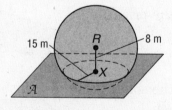

20. Find the surface area of this
hemisphere to the nearest tenth.

20._____

Bonus The surface area of the exterior of a hollow rubber ball is
16π square inches. The rubber is $\frac{1}{4}$ inch thick. Find the
surface area of the interior of the ball.

B: _____

12 **Chapter 12 Test, Form 2D**

Assessment

1. Given the corner view of a figure, sketch the back view.

1. _____

2. Name the edges of the solid.

2. _____

3. Identify the solid.

3. _____

4. How many edges does a cube have?

4. _____

5. Draw a net for the solid.

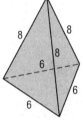

5. _____

6. Find the surface area of the solid.

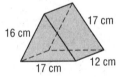

6. _____

7. Find the lateral area of a regular pentagonal prism if the perimeter of the base is 50 inches and the height is 15 inches.

7. _____

8. Find the surface area of the prism.

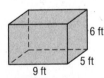

8. _____

9. A gallon of paint covers 300 square feet. How many gallons are needed to paint the walls and bottom of a rectangular swimming pool whose length is 25 feet, width is 16 feet, and depth is 4 feet? Round to the next whole gallon.

9. _____

10. Find the surface area of the solid.

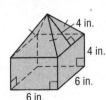

10. _____

11. A right cylinder has a diameter of 23.6 meters and a height of 11.4 meters. Find the lateral area of the cylinder. Round to the nearest tenth.

11. _____

12. The surface area of a right cylinder is 252π square feet and the height is 11 feet. Find the radius of the cylinder.

12. _____

For Questions 13 and 14, use a regular octagonal pyramid with base edges 9 feet long, slant height 15 feet, and a base with an apothem of 10.86 feet.

13. Find the lateral area.

13. _____

14. Find the surface area to the nearest tenth.

14. _____

15. Find the lateral area of the solid. Round to the nearest tenth.

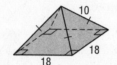

15. _____

16. The surface area of a regular decagonal pyramid is 1800 square feet, the area of the base is 120 square feet, and the slant height is 15 feet. Find the length of each side of the base of the pyramid. Round to the nearest tenth.

16. _____

For Questions 17 and 18, use a cone with a radius of 5 centimeters and a height of 12 centimeters. Round to the nearest tenth.

17. Find the lateral area.

17. _____

18. Find the surface area.

18. _____

19. Plane $\mathcal{A}$ intersects sphere B in $\odot C$. Find BC.

19. _____

20. Find the surface area of the hemisphere. Round to the nearest tenth.

20. _____

Bonus The length of each side of a cube is 6 inches long. Find the surface area of a sphere inscribed in the cube. Round to the nearest tenth.

B: _____

12 Chapter 12 Test, Form 3

Assessment

1. Draw the back view of a figure given its orthographic drawing.

top view   left view   front view   right view

1. _____

2. Name the bases of the solid.

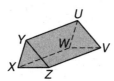

2. _____

3. Identify the solid.

3. _____

4. How many faces does an icosahedron have?

4. _____

5. Draw a net for the solid.

5. _____

6. Find the surface area of the solid.

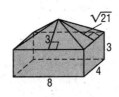

6. _____

7. Find the lateral area of a triangular prism with a right triangular base with legs that measure 2 feet and 3 feet and a height of 7 feet.

7. _____

8. Find the surface area of the prism.

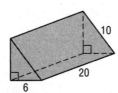

8. _____

For Questions 9 and 10, use a right cylinder with a diameter of 96.4 feet and a height of 58.9 feet. Round to the nearest tenth.

9. Find the lateral area.

9. _____

10. Find the surface area.

10. _____

11. A soup can has a height of six inches and a diameter of two inches. Find the area of the label assuming it takes up the entire face of the can. Round to the nearest tenth.

11. _____

**For Questions 12 and 13, refer to the solid.
Round to the nearest tenth if necessary.**

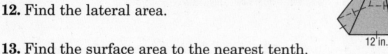

12. Find the lateral area.

12._____

13. Find the surface area to the nearest tenth.

13._____

14. If the length of each side of a cube is tripled, what happens to the surface area?

14._____

**For Questions 15 and 16, use a right circular cone with a
radius of 7 inches and a height of 8 inches. Round to the
nearest tenth.**

15. Find the lateral area.

15._____

16. Find the surface area.

16._____

17. Find the surface area of this frustum of a cone, to the nearest tenth.

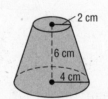

17._____

18. Parallel planes A and B intersect sphere C in circles D and E and $DC = 6$. Find CE.

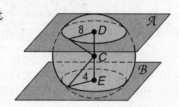

18._____

19. Write a formula for the surface area of a hemisphere in terms of π and the radius r.

19._____

20. Find the surface area of the solid. Round to the nearest square foot.

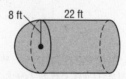

20._____

Bonus Find the surface area of the solid to the nearest square foot. Do not include the area of the base.

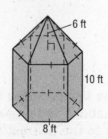

B: _____

12 **Chapter 12 Extended-Response Test**

Demonstrate your knowledge by giving a clear, concise solution to each problem. Be sure to include all relevant drawings and justify your answers. You may show your solution in more than one way or investigate beyond the requirements of the problem.

1. a. Complete this chart.

Figure	No. of Edges (e)	No. of Faces (f)	No. of Vertices (v)	f + v
Triangular Pyramid	6	4	4	8
Triangular Prism				
Cube				
Square Pyramid				
Hexagonal Prism				
Hexagonal Pyramid				

   b. Write a formula relating the number of edges to the number of faces and vertices.

2. Explain the difference between the lateral area and the surface area of a prism.

3. a. Draw and label a pyramid.

   b. Name the base.

   c. Name the lateral faces.

   d. Draw a net for your pyramid.

4. Draw an oblique cylinder and a right cylinder.

5. a. Draw and label the dimensions of a solid figure composed of three or more different solids studied in this chapter.

   b. Find the surface area.

6. Write a practical application problem involving the surface area or lateral area of a solid figure studied in this chapter.

12 Standardized Test Practice

(Chapters 1–10)

Part 1: Multiple Choice

Instructions: Fill in the appropriate circle for the best answer.

1. Which method could you use to prove $\overline{BE} \cong \overline{AC}$ if $AF = BF$? (Lesson 4-5)

   A Show that $\triangle ABE \cong \triangle BAC$ by SSS, then $\overline{BE} \cong \overline{AC}$ by CPCTC.
   B Show that $\triangle ABE \cong \triangle BAC$ by ASA, then $\overline{BE} \cong \overline{AC}$ by CPCTC.
   C Show that $\triangle BFE \cong \triangle AFC$ by SAS, then $\overline{BE} \cong \overline{AC}$ by CPCTC.
   D Show that $\triangle ABE \cong \triangle BAC$ by AAS, then $\overline{BE} \cong \overline{AC}$ by CPCTC.

   1. Ⓐ Ⓑ Ⓒ Ⓓ

2. Find a. (Lesson 6-3)

   F 28.5   **H** 12.6
   G 6.3   **J** 14

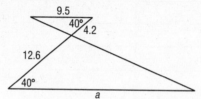

   2. Ⓕ Ⓖ Ⓗ Ⓙ

3. Find r. (Lesson 7-6)

   A about 34.0   **C** about 11.8
   B about 8.9   **D** about 6.6

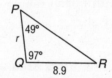

   3. Ⓐ Ⓑ Ⓒ Ⓓ

4. A square has side length 18 centimeters. Find the area of the square. (Lesson 8-5)

   F 36 cm^2 **G** 40 cm^2 **H** 81 cm^2 **J** 324 cm^2

   4. Ⓕ Ⓖ Ⓗ Ⓙ

5. What can you assume from the figure? (Lesson 10-3)

   A $\triangle ABC$ is isosceles.
   B $\triangle ABC$ is equilateral.
   C $DF = EG$
   D radius of $\odot O = x + y$

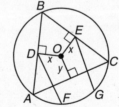

   5. Ⓐ Ⓑ Ⓒ Ⓓ

6. Points D, E, and F are on a circle so that $m\widehat{DEF} = 210$. Suppose point G is randomly located on the same circle so that it does not coincide with D, E, or F. What is the probability that $m\angle DGF = 105$? (Lesson 10-4)

   F $\dfrac{7}{12}$ **G** $\dfrac{5}{12}$ **H** 1   **J** $\dfrac{3}{4}$

   6. Ⓕ Ⓖ Ⓗ Ⓙ

7. Which net could be folded into a triangular prism? (Lesson 12-2)

   A   **B**   **C**   **D**

   7. Ⓐ Ⓑ Ⓒ Ⓓ

8. Find the surface area of a square pyramid with a height of 9 centimeters and base with a side measuring 24 centimeters. (Lesson 12-5)

   F 1296 cm^2 **G** 1806 cm^2 **H** 2016 cm^2 **J** 8640 cm^2

   8. Ⓕ Ⓖ Ⓗ Ⓙ

12 Standardized Test Practice *(continued)*

9. Find y to the nearest centimeter. (Lesson 7-7)

  A 19 cm   **C** 34 cm

  B 28 cm   **D** 37 cm

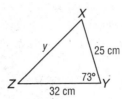

9. Ⓐ Ⓑ Ⓒ Ⓓ

10. A plane figure is the locus of all points in a plane equidistant from point B. What is the shape of this figure? (Lesson 10-1)

  F Square   **G** Cylinder   **H** Rhombus   **J** Circle

10. Ⓕ Ⓖ Ⓗ Ⓙ

11. Find $m\angle C$. (Lesson 10-6)

  A 18°   **C** 28°

  B 25°   **D** 60°

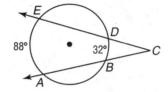

11. Ⓐ Ⓑ Ⓒ Ⓓ

12. Find the area of the figure. (Lesson 11-1)

  F 76 cm²   **H** 88 cm²

  G 80 cm²   **J** 92 cm²

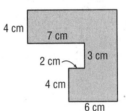

12. Ⓕ Ⓖ Ⓗ Ⓙ

Part 2: Griddable

Instructions: Enter your answer by writing each digit of the answer in a column box and then shading in the appropriate circle that corresponds to that entry.

13. Quadrilateral $PQSR$ is a rectangle. Find a. (Lesson 8-4)

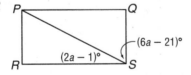

13.

				.			
⓪	⓪	⓪	⓪		⓪	⓪	⓪
①	①	①	①		①	①	①
②	②	②	②		②	②	②
③	③	③	③		③	③	③
④	④	④	④		④	④	④
⑤	⑤	⑤	⑤		⑤	⑤	⑤
⑥	⑥	⑥	⑥		⑥	⑥	⑥
⑦	⑦	⑦	⑦		⑦	⑦	⑦
⑧	⑧	⑧	⑧		⑧	⑧	⑧
⑨	⑨	⑨	⑨		⑨	⑨	⑨

14. Find x. Assume that segments that appear tangent are tangent. (Lesson 10-5)

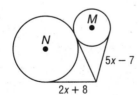

14.

				.			
⓪	⓪	⓪	⓪		⓪	⓪	⓪
①	①	①	①		①	①	①
②	②	②	②		②	②	②
③	③	③	③		③	③	③
④	④	④	④		④	④	④
⑤	⑤	⑤	⑤		⑤	⑤	⑤
⑥	⑥	⑥	⑥		⑥	⑥	⑥
⑦	⑦	⑦	⑦		⑦	⑦	⑦
⑧	⑧	⑧	⑧		⑧	⑧	⑧
⑨	⑨	⑨	⑨		⑨	⑨	⑨

Assessment

12 **Standardized Test Practice** *(continued)* SCORE _____

Part 3: Short Response

Instructions: Write your answer in the space provided.

---

15. Find the length of $\overset{\frown}{SR}$ to the nearest tenth. (Lesson 10-2)

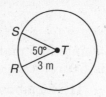

15. _____

16. Find x. (Lesson 10-7)

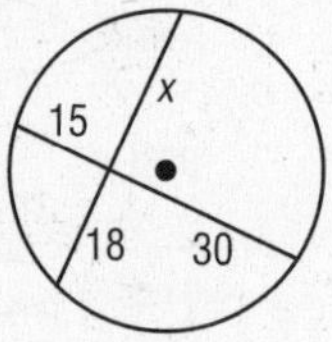

16. _____

17. Find the area of the shaded region to the nearest tenth. (Lesson 11-3)

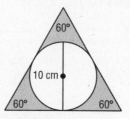

17. _____

18. Identify the solid. (Lesson 12-1)

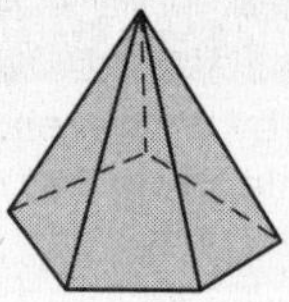

18. _____

19. A right circular cone has a slant height of 15 inches and a radius that is 25 inches long. Find the surface area of the cone. Round to the nearest tenth. (Lesson 12-6)

19. _____

20. A ball has a diameter of 26.5 centimeters. Find the surface area of the ball. Round to the nearest tenth. (Lesson 12-7)

20. _____

21. Find the following measurements for a sphere with a diameter of 66 meters. Round to the nearest tenth. (Lesson 12-7)

a. Surface area to the nearest tenth.

21a. _____

b. Circumference of the great circle to the nearest tenth.

21b. _____

c. Area of the great circle to the nearest tenth.

21c. _____

d. Surface area of the hemisphere to the nearest tenth.

21d. _____

NAME _____ DATE _____ PERIOD _____

12 Anticipation Guide

Extending Surface Area

Step 1 *Before you begin Chapter 12*

- Read each statement.
- Decide whether you Agree (A) or Disagree (D) with the statement.
- Write A or D in the first column OR if you are not sure whether you agree or disagree, write NS (Not Sure).

STEP 1 A, D, or NS	Statement	STEP 2 A or D
	1. Prisms, pyramids, cylinders, and cones are all polyhedrons.	D
	2. The net of a pyramid could contain a square and four triangles.	A
	3. The lateral area of a prism is equal to the sum of the areas of each face.	D
	4. The axis of an oblique cylinder is different than the height of the cylinder.	A
	5. The surface area of a right cylinder with radius r and height h is $2\pi rh + 2\pi r^2$.	A
	6. The slant height and height of a regular pyramid are the same.	D
	7. Since a pyramid has only one base, its surface area equals its lateral area.	D
	8. The lateral area of a cone equals the product of π, the radius, and the height of the cone.	D
	9. To find the surface area of a sphere with radius r, multiply πr^2 by 4.	A
	10. A *great circle* of a sphere is any circle formed by the intersection of a plane and the sphere.	D

Step 2 *After you complete Chapter 12*

- Reread each statement and complete the last column by entering an A or a D.
- Did any of your opinions about the statements change from the first column?
- For those statements that you mark with a D, use a piece of paper to write an example of why you disagree.

Chapter 12   3   *Glencoe Geometry*

NAME _____ DATE _____ PERIOD _____

12-1 Lesson Reading Guide

Representations of Three-Dimensional Figures

Get Ready For the Lesson

Read the introduction to Lesson 12-1 in your textbook.

Artists use three-point perspective to draw three-dimensional objects with a high degree of realism. Why do three-point perspective drawings look more realistic than isometric drawings? **Sample answer: When we view things in real life they appear smaller if they are farther away and parallel lines appear to meet at the horizon.**

Read the Lesson

Complete the following table. 1–4. See students' work.

Word	Definition
1. corner view	
2. perspective view	
3. cross section	
4. reflection symmetry	

5. A three-point perspective drawing has three <u>vanishing</u> points. Each of these points is aligned with the <u>height</u>, width, and length of the figure.

6. A cross section of a solid occurs when a <u>plane</u> intersects a solid figure.

Remember What You Learned

7. Look up the word isometry in a dictionary. Compare its definition with the definition of corner view and perspective view. Why are corner views considered isometric views but three-dimensional point perspective views not considered isometric views? **Sample answer: an isometry is a distance preserving transformation. Corner views represent the actual distances of figures, while three-point perspective views represent the apparent distances of figures.**

Chapter 12   5   *Glencoe Geometry*

NAME _____ DATE _____ PERIOD _____

12-1 Study Guide and Intervention (continued)

Representations of Three-Dimensional Figures

Cross-Sections The intersection of a solid and a plane is called a cross-section of the solid. The shape of a cross-section depends upon the shape of the solid figure, the angle of the plane makes with the base of the solid figure, and where the plane interests the figure.

Example

There are several interesting shapes that are cross-sections of a cone. Determine the shape resulting from each cross-section of the cone.

a. If the plane is parallel to the base of the cone, then the resulting cross-section will be a circle.

b. If the plane cuts through the cone perpendicular to the base and through the center of the cone, then the resulting cross-section will be a triangle.

c. If the plane cuts across the entire cone, then the resulting cross-section will be an ellipse.

Top View

Side View

Angle View

Exercises

Determine the shape resulting from each cross section of the cylinder.

1. circle

2. ellipse

3. rectangle

NAME _____ DATE _____ PERIOD _____

12-1 Study Guide and Intervention (continued)

Representations of Three-Dimensional Figures

Drawings of Three-Dimensional Figures To work with a three-dimensional object, it can be useful to draw different views. The view of a figure from a corner is called the **corner view** or **perspective view.** An orthographic drawing includes a two-dimensional top view, left view, front view, and right view of a three-dimensional.

Example 1 Use isometric dot paper to sketch a triangular prism with 3-4-5 right triangles as bases and with a height of 3 units.

Step 1 Draw $\overline{AB}$ at 3 units and draw $\overline{AC}$ at 4 units.
Step 2 Draw $\overline{AD}$, $\overline{BE}$, and $\overline{CF}$, each at 3 units.
Step 3 Draw $\overline{BC}$ and $\triangle DEF$.

Example 2 Draw the back view of the figure given the orthogonal drawing.

• The top view indicates two columns.
• The right and left views indicate that the height of figure is three blocks.
• The front view indicates that the columns have heights 2 and 3 blocks.

Use blocks to make a model of the object. Then use your model to draw the back view. The back view indicates that the columns have heights 3 and 2 blocks.

Exercises

Sketch each solid using isometric dot paper.

1. cube with edge 4

2. rectangular prism 1 unit high, 5 units long, and 4 units wide

Draw the back view and corner view of a figure given each orthographic drawing.

3.

4.

Answers (Lesson 12–1)

12-1 Skills Practice

Representations of Three-Dimensional Figures

Sketch each solid using isometric dot paper.

1. cube 2 units on each edge

2. rectangular prism 2 units high, 5 units long, and 2 units wide

Draw the back view and corner view of a figure given each orthogonal drawing.

3. top view, left view, front view, right view, back view, corner view

4. top view, left view, front view, right view, back view, corner view

Determine the shape resulting from each cross section of the square prism.

5. square

6. rectangle

7. triangle

8. rectangle

12-1 Practice

Representations of Three-Dimensional Figures

Sketch each solid using isometric dot paper.

1. rectangular prism 3 units high, 3 units long, and 2 units wide

2. triangular prism 3 units high, whose bases are right triangles with legs 2 units and 4 units long

Draw the back view and corner view of a figure given each orthogonal drawing.

3. top view, left view, front view, right view, back view, corner view

4. top view, left view, front view, right view, back view, corner view

Determine the cross-section resulting from the horizontal and vertical slice of each solid.

5. circle, circle

6. rectangle, trapezoid

7. **SPHERES** Consider the sphere in Exercise 5. Based on the cross-section resulting from the horizontal and vertical slice of the sphere, make a conjecture about all spherical cross-sections.
All spherical cross-sections are circles.

8. **MINERALS** Pyrite, also known as fool's gold, can form crystals that are perfect cubes. Suppose a gemologist wants to cut a cube of pyrite to get a square and a rectangular face. What cuts should be made to get each of the shapes? Illustrate your answers.
a cut parallel to the bases to get a square
a cut through diagonally opposite top and bottom edges to get a rectangle

Answers

NAME ______________________ DATE __________ PERIOD _____

12-1 Word Problem Practice

Representations of Three-Dimensional Figures

1. **LABELS** Jamal removes the label from a cylindrical soup can to earn points for his school. Sketch the shape of the label.

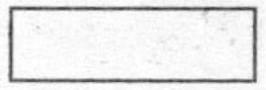

2. **BLOCKS** Margot's three-year-old son made the magnetic block sculpture shown below in corner view.

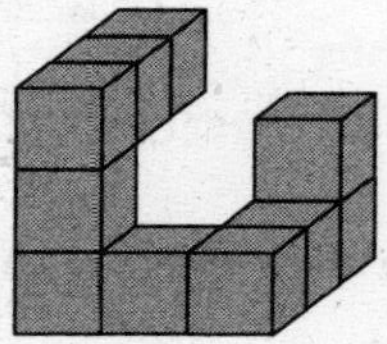

Draw the right view of the sculpture.

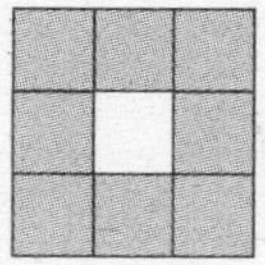

3. **CUBES** Nathan marks the midpoints of three edges of a cube as shown. He then slices the cube along a plane that contains these three points. Describe the resulting cross section.

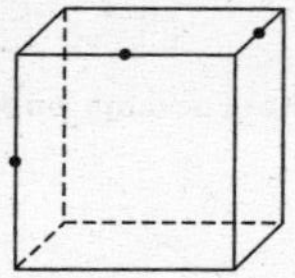

regular hexagon

4. **ENGINEERING** Stephanie needs an object whose top view is a circle and whose left and front views are squares. Describe an object that will satisfy these conditions.
Sample answer: A cylinder with its height equal to its diameter.

DESK SUPPORTS For Exercises 5-7, use the following information.

The figure shows the support for a desk.

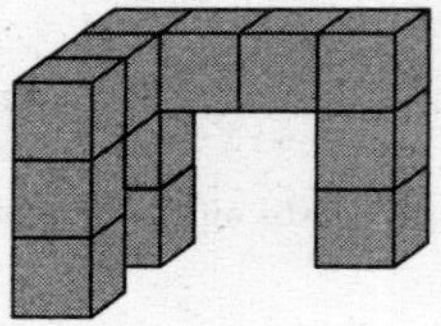

5. Draw the top view.

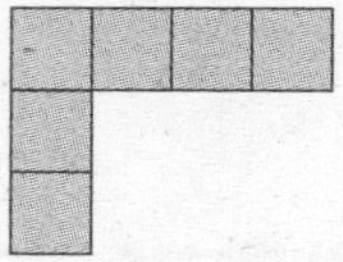

6. Draw the front view.

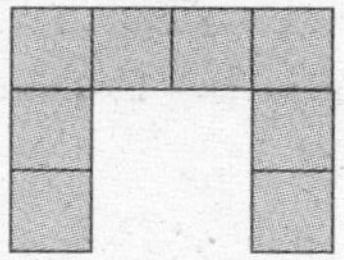

7. Draw the right view.

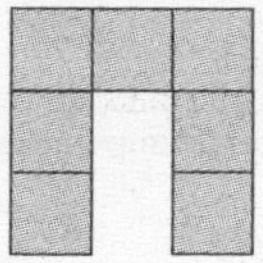

NAME ______________________ DATE __________ PERIOD _____

12-1 Enrichment

Drawing Solids on Isometric Dot Paper

Isometric dot paper is helpful for drawing solids. Remember to use dashed lines for hidden edges.

For each solid shown, draw another solid whose dimensions are twice as large.

1.

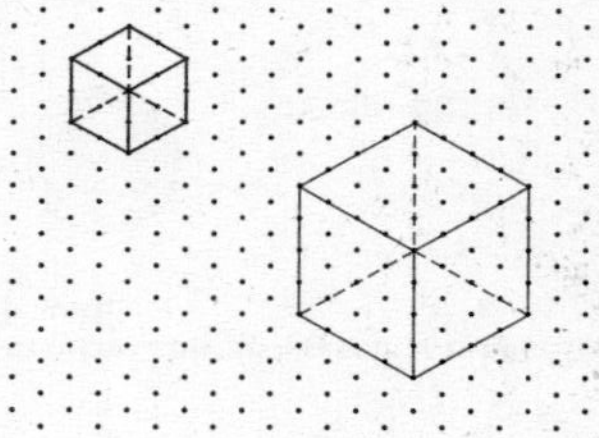

2.

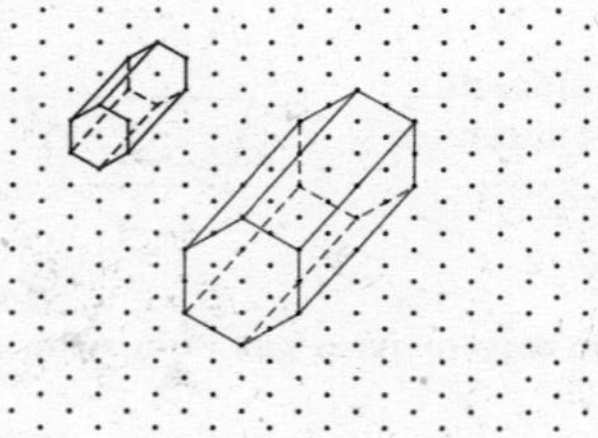

3.

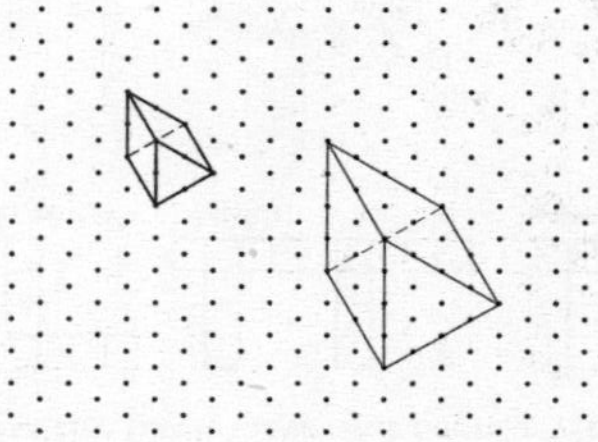

4.

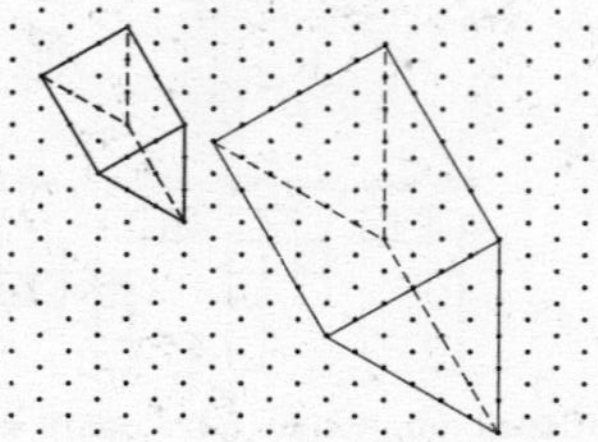

5.

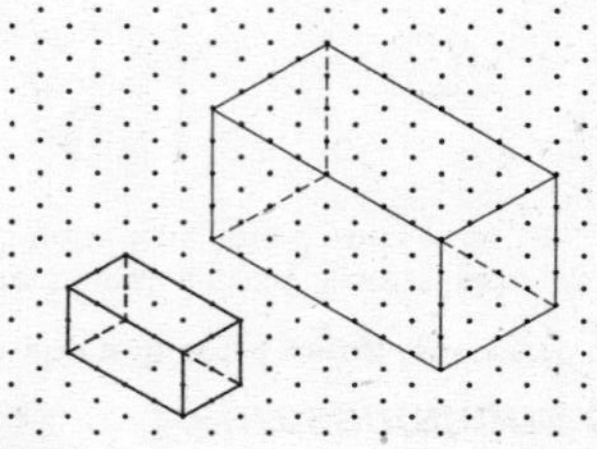

6.

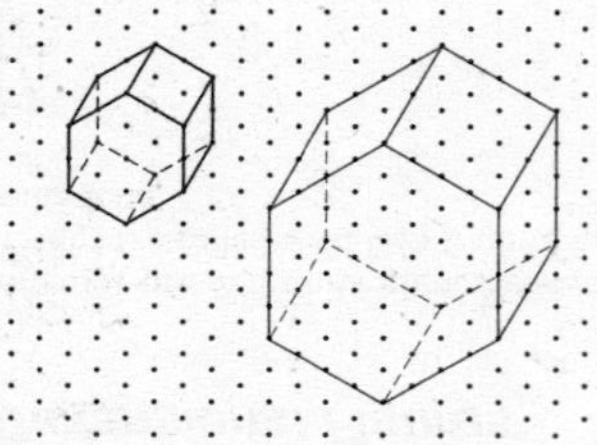

12-1 Graphing Calculator Activity

Perspective Drawings

The science of perspective drawing studies how to draw a three-dimensional object on a two-dimensional page. This science became highly refined during the Renaissance with the work of artists such as Albrecht Dürer and Leonardo da Vinci.

Today, computers are often used to make perspective drawings, particularly elaborate graphics used in television and movies. The three-dimensional coordinates of objects are figured. Then algebra is used to transform these into two-dimensional coordinates. The graph of these new coordinates is called a *projection*.

The formulas below will draw one type of projection in which the *y*-axis is drawn horizontally, the *z*-axis vertically, and the *x*-axis at an angle of $a°$ with the *y*-axis. If the three-dimensional coordinates of a point are (x, y, z), then the projection coordinates (X, Y) are given by

$$X = x(-\cos a) + y \text{ and } Y = x(-\sin a) + z.$$

Although this type of projection gives a fairly good perspective drawing, it does distort some lengths.

1. The drawing with the coordinates given below is a cube.

$A(5, 0, 5)$, $B(5, 5, 5)$, $C(5, 5, 0)$, $D(5, 0, 0)$,
$E(0, 0, 5)$, $F(0, 5, 5)$, $G(0, 5, 0)$, $H(0, 0, 0)$

Use the formulas above to find the projection coordinates of each point, using $a = 45$. Round projection coordinates to the nearest integer. Graph the cube on a graphing calculator. Make a sketch of the display.

$A'(\_\_,\_\_)$ $B'(\_\_,\_\_)$ $C'(\_\_,\_\_)$ $D'(\_\_,\_\_)$ $E'(\_\_,\_\_)$ $F'(\_\_,\_\_)$
$G'(\_\_,\_\_)$ $H'(\_\_,\_\_)$
$A'(-4, 1)$, $B'(1, 1)$, $C'(1, -4)$, $D'(-4, -4)$, $E'(0, 5)$, $F'(5, 5)$, $G'(5, 0)$ $H'(0,0)$;
For sketches, see students' work.

2. The points $A(10, 2, 0)$, $B(10, 10, 0)$, $C(2, 10, 0)$, and $D(3, 3, 4)$ are vertices of a pyramid. Find the projection coordinates, using $a = 25$. Round coordinates to the nearest integer. Then graph the pyramid on a graphing calculator by drawing $\overline{A'B'}$, $\overline{B'C'}$, $\overline{C'D'}$, $\overline{D'A'}$, and $\overline{DB'}$. Make a sketch of the display.

$A'(\_\_,\_\_)$ $B'(\_\_,\_\_)$ $C'(\_\_,\_\_)$ $D'(\_\_,\_\_)$
$A'(-7, -4)$, $B'(1, -4)$, $C'(8, -1)$, $D'(0, 3)$; **for sketches, see students' work.**

12-2 Lesson Reading Guide

Surface Areas of Prisms

Get Ready for the Lesson

Read the introduction to Lesson 12-2 in your textbook.

How could the architects figure out lateral area of the building? **Sample answer: Find the area of each side by multiplying its width by the building height. Add these areas together.**

Read the Lesson

1. Determine whether each sentence is *always*, *sometimes*, or *never* true.
   a. A base of a prism is a face of the prism. **always**
   b. A face of a prism is a base of the prism. **sometimes**
   c. The lateral faces of a prism are rectangles. **sometimes**
   d. If a base of a prism has *n* vertices, then the prism has *n* faces. **never**
   e. If a base of a prism has *n* vertices, then the prism has *n* lateral edges. **always**
   f. In a right prism, the lateral edges are also altitudes. **always**
   g. The bases of a prism are congruent regular polygons. **sometimes**
   h. Any two lateral edges of a prism are perpendicular to each other. **never**
   i. In a rectangular prism, any pair of opposite faces can be called the bases. **always**
   j. All of the lateral faces of a prism are congruent to each other. **sometimes**

2. Explain the difference between the *lateral area* of a prism and the *surface area* of a prism. Your explanation should apply to both right and oblique prisms. Do not use any formulas in your explanation. **Sample answer: The lateral area is the sum of the areas of lateral faces. The surface area is the sum of the areas of all the faces, including both the lateral faces and the bases.**

3. Refer to the figure.

   a. Name this solid with as specific a name as possible. **right regular pentagonal prism**
   b. Name the bases of the solid. **pentagons *ABCDE* and *FGHIJ***
   c. Name the lateral faces. **rectangles *ABGF, BCHG, CDIH, DEJI,* and *EAFJ***
   d. Name the edges. $\overline{AF}$, $\overline{BG}$, $\overline{CH}$, $\overline{DI}$, $\overline{EJ}$, $\overline{AB}$, $\overline{BC}$, $\overline{CD}$, $\overline{DE}$, $\overline{EA}$, $\overline{FG}$, $\overline{GH}$, $\overline{HI}$, $\overline{IJ}$, $\overline{JF}$
   e. Name an altitude of the solid. $\overline{AF}$, $\overline{BG}$, $\overline{CH}$, $\overline{DI}$, or $\overline{EJ}$
   f. If *a* represents the area of one of the bases, *P* represents the perimeter of one of the bases, and $x = AF$, write an expression for the surface area of the solid that involves *a, P,* and *x*. $Px + 2a$

Remember What You Learned

4. A good way to remember a new mathematical term is to relate it to an everyday use of the same word. How can the way the word *lateral* is used in sports help you remember the meaning of the *lateral area* of a solid? **Sample answer: In football, a pass thrown to the *side* is called a *lateral pass.* In geometry, the *lateral area* is the "side area," or the sum of the areas of all the side surfaces of the solid (the surfaces other than the bases).**

12-2 Study Guide and Intervention *(continued)*

Surface Areas of Prisms

Surface Areas of Prisms The surface area of a prism is the lateral area of the prism plus the areas of the bases.

Surface Area of a Prism	If the total surface area of a prism is T square units, its height is h units, and each base has an area of B square units and a perimeter of P units, then $T = L + 2B$.

Example Find the surface area of the triangular prism above.

Find the lateral area of the prism.

$L = Ph$ Lateral area of a prism
$= (18)(10)$ $P = 18, h = 10$
$= 180$ cm²   Multiply.

Find the area of each base. Use the Pythagorean Theorem to find the height of the triangular base.

$h^2 + 3^2 = 6^2$ Pythagorean Theorem
$h^2 = 27$ Simplify.
$h = 3\sqrt{3}$ Take the square root of each side.
$B = \frac{1}{2} \times \text{base} \times \text{height}$ Area of a triangle
$= \frac{1}{2}(6)(3\sqrt{3})$ or 15.6 cm²

The total area is the lateral area plus the area of the two bases.

$T = 180 + 2(15.6)$ Substitution
$= 211.2$ cm²   Simplify.

Exercises

Find the surface area of each prism. Round to the nearest tenth if necessary.

1. 1024 in²

2. 84 m²

3. 324 m²

4. 619.1 in²

5. 415.4 in²

6. 384 m²

12-2 Study Guide and Intervention *(continued)*

Surface Areas of Prisms

Lateral Areas of Prisms Here are some characteristics of prisms.

- The bases are parallel and congruent.
- The **lateral faces** are the faces that are not bases.
- The lateral faces intersect at **lateral edges**, which are parallel.
- The **altitude** of a prism is a segment that is perpendicular to the bases with an endpoint in each base.
- For a **right prism**, the lateral edges are perpendicular to the bases. Otherwise, the prism is **oblique**.

altitude, lateral face, lateral edge, pentagonal prism

Lateral Area of a Prism	If a prism has a lateral area of L square units, a height of h units, and each base has a perimeter of P units, then $L = Ph$.

Example Find the lateral area of the regular pentagonal prism above if each base has a perimeter of 75 centimeters and the altitude is 10 centimeters.

$L = Ph$ Lateral area of a prism
$= 75(10)$ $P = 75, h = 10$
$= 750$ Multiply.

The lateral area is 750 square centimeters.

Exercises

Find the lateral area of each prism.

1. 120 m²

2. 460 in² (8 in. × 15 in. base); 400 in² (10 in. × 15 in. base); 540 in² (10 in. × 8 in. base)

3. 540 in²

4. 588 cm²

5. 128 in² (rectangular base) 192 in² (square base)

6. 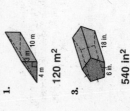 384 m²

Left page

NAME _____ DATE _____ PERIOD _____

12-2 Skills Practice

Surface Areas of Prisms

Find the lateral area of each prism.

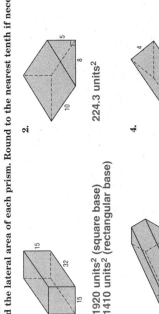

1. **480 units² (square base)**
   528 units² (rectangular base)

2. **240 units² (8 × 12 base)**
   288 units² (12 × 6 base)
   336 units² (8 × 6 base)

3. **120 units²**

4. **324 units²**

Find the surface area of each prism. Round to the nearest tenth if necessary.

5. **600 units²**

6. **782 units²**

7. **312.2 units²**

8. **85.2 units²**

Right page

NAME _____ DATE _____ PERIOD _____

12-2 Practice

Surface Areas of Prisms

Find the lateral area of each prism. Round to the nearest tenth if necessary.

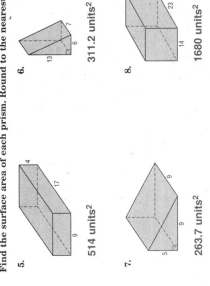

1. **1920 units² (square base)**
   1410 units² (rectangular base)

2. **224.3 units²**

3. **132 units²**

4. **123.5 units²**

Find the surface area of each prism. Round to the nearest tenth if necessary.

5. **514 units²**

6. **311.2 units²**

7. **263.7 units²**

8. **1680 units²**

9. **CRAFTS** Becca made a rectangular jewelry box in her art class and plans to cover it in red silk. If the jewelry box is $6\frac{1}{2}$ inches long, $4\frac{1}{2}$ inches wide, and 3 inches high, find the surface area that will be covered. **$124\frac{1}{2}$ in²**

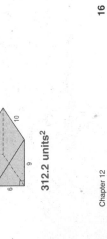
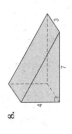
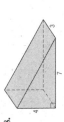

NAME _____ DATE _____ PERIOD _____

12-2 Word Problem Practice

Surface Areas of Prisms

1. **LOGOS** The Z company specializes in caring for zebras. They want to make a 3-dimensional "Z" to put in front of their company headquarters. The "Z" is 15 inches thick and the perimeter of the base is 390 inches.

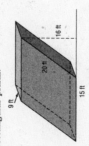

What is the lateral surface area of this "Z"?
5850 in²

2. **STAIRWELLS** Management decides to enclose stairs connecting the first and second floors of a parking garage in a stairwell shaped like an oblique rectangular prism.

What is the lateral surface area of the stairwell?
840 ft²

3. **CAKES** A cake is a rectangular prism with height 4 inches and base 12 inches by 15 inches. Wallace wants to apply frosting to the sides and the top of the cake. What is the surface area of the part of the cake that will have frosting?
396 in²

4. **CANDY** A candy maker packages one of its products in a triangular prism. The height of the prism is 10 inches. The base is an equilateral triangle with side length 3 inches. What is the surface area of the package? Round your answer to the nearest hundredth.
97.79 in²

WOOD PLANKS For Exercises 5-8, use the following information.
A wood plank is a rectangular prism with length 10 feet and base dimensions 2 inches by 4 inches.

5. What is the surface area of the plank in square inches?
1456 in²

6. Katrina cuts the plank in half lengthwise and obtains two wood planks, each 5 feet long. What is the total surface area of both planks?
1472 in²

7. If instead, Katrina had cut the plank into N equal pieces lengthwise, what would be the total surface area of all N pieces?
1440 + 16N in²

8. Katrina wants to cut the plank into two rectangular pieces in a way that will give her the greatest total surface area for the pieces. How should she cut the plank?
along the plane parallel to the side with dimensions 4 in by 10 ft

---

NAME _____ DATE _____ PERIOD _____

12-2 Enrichment

Cross Sections of Prisms

When a plane intersects a solid figure to form a two-dimensional figure, the results is called a **cross section**. The figure at the right shows a plane intersecting a cube. The cross section is a hexagon.

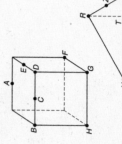

For each right prism, connect the labeled points in alphabetical order to show a cross section. Then identify the polygon.

1. **rectangle**
2. **triangle**
3. **trapezoid**

Refer to the right prisms shown at the right. In the rectangular prism, A and C are midpoints. Identify the cross-section polygon formed by a plane containing the given points.

4. A, C, H **rectangle**
5. C, E, G **triangle**
6. H, C, E, F **trapezoid**
7. H, A, E **pentagon**
8. B, D, F **rectangle**
9. V, X, R **triangle**
10. R, T, Y **rectangle**
11. R, S, W **trapezoid**

NAME _____ DATE _____ PERIOD _____

12-3 Lesson Reading Guide

Surface Areas of Cylinders

Get Ready for the Lesson

Read the introduction to Lesson 12-3 in your textbook.

If the surface area of the half-pipe includes an added flat section in the middle, then how does the surface area of the half-pipe compare to the full-pipe? **It is more than half the surface area of the full-pipe.**

Read the Lesson

1. Underline the correct word or phrase to form a true statement.

   a. The bases of a cylinder are (rectangles/<u>regular polygons/circles</u>).

   b. The (<u>axis</u>/radius/diameter) of a cylinder is the segment whose endpoints are the centers of the bases.

   c. The net of a cylinder is composed of two congruent (<u>rectangles/circles</u>) and one (<u>rectangle</u>/semicircle).

   d. In a right cylinder, the axis of the cylinder is also a(n) (base/<u>lateral edge/altitude</u>).

   e. A cylinder that is not a right cylinder is called an (acute/obtuse/<u>oblique</u>) cylinder.

2. Match each description from the first column with an expression from the second column that represents its value.

   a. the lateral area of a right cylinder in which the radius of each base is x cm and the length of the axis is y cm **v**

   b. the surface area of a right prism with square bases in which the length of a side of a base is x cm and the length of a lateral edge is y cm **i**

   c. the surface area of a right cylinder in which the radius of a base is x cm and the height is y cm **ii**

   d. the surface area of regular hexahedron (cube) in which the length of each edge is x cm **iv**

   e. the lateral area of a triangular prism in which the bases are equilateral triangles with side length x cm and the height is y cm **iii**

   f. the surface area of a right cylinder in which the diameter of the base is x cm and the length of the axis is y cm **vi**

   i. $(2x^2 + 4xy)$ cm^2
   ii. $(2\pi xy + 2\pi x^2)$ cm^2
   iii. $3xy$ cm^2
   iv. $6x^2$ cm^2
   v. $2\pi xy$ cm^2
   vi. $\left(\dfrac{\pi x^2}{2} + \pi xy\right)$ cm^2

Remember What You Learned

3. Often the best way to remember a mathematical formula is to think about where the different parts of the formula come from. How can you use this approach to remember the formula for the surface area of a cylinder? **Sample answer: Think about the net for a cylinder. The two bases are circles, each with radius r, so the sum of their areas is $2\pi r^2$. The lateral surface is a rectangle whose dimensions are the circumference $2\pi r$ of the circular base and the height h of the cylinder, so the lateral area is $2\pi rh$. Add the lateral area and the area of the two bases to get the surface area of the cylinder: $2\pi rh + 2\pi r^2$.**

NAME _____ DATE _____ PERIOD _____

12-3 Study Guide and Intervention

Surface Areas of Cylinders

Lateral Areas of Cylinders A **cylinder** is a solid whose bases are congruent circles that lie in parallel planes. The **axis** of a cylinder is the segment whose endpoints are the centers of these circles. For a **right cylinder**, the axis and the altitude of the cylinder are equal. The lateral area of a right cylinder is the circumference of the cylinder multiplied by the height.

Lateral Area of a Cylinder	If a cylinder has a lateral area of L square units, a height of h units, and the bases have radii of r units, then $L = 2\pi rh$.

Example **Find the lateral area of the cylinder above if the radius of the base is 6 centimeters and the height is 14 centimeters.**

$$L = 2\pi rh \qquad \text{Lateral area of a cylinder}$$
$$= 2\pi(6)(14) \qquad \text{Substitution}$$
$$\approx 527.8 \qquad \text{Simplify.}$$

The lateral area is about 527.8 square centimeters.

Exercises

Find the lateral area of each cylinder. Round to the nearest tenth.

1.
   4 cm, 12 cm
   301.6 cm^2

2.
   10 in., 6 in.
   377.0 in^2

3.
   3 cm, 3 cm, 6 cm
   113.1 cm^2

4.
   8 cm, 20 cm
   502.7 cm^2

5. 12 m, 4 m
   150.8 m^2

6. 2 m, 1 m
   12.6 m^2

12-3 Study Guide and Intervention (continued)

NAME _____ DATE _____ PERIOD _____

Surface Areas of Cylinders

Surface Areas of Cylinders The surface area of a cylinder is the lateral area of the cylinder plus the areas of the bases.

| Surface Area of a Cylinder | If a cylinder has a surface area of T square units, a height of h units, and the bases have radii of r units, then $T = 2\pi rh + 2\pi r^2$. |

Example **Find the surface area of the cylinder.**

Find the lateral area of the cylinder. If the diameter is 12 centimeters, then the radius is 6 centimeters.

$L = Ph$ Lateral area of a cylinder
$= (2\pi r)h$ $P = 2\pi r$
$= 2\pi(6)(14)$ $r = 6, h = 14$
≈ 527.8 Simplify.

Find the area of each base.

$B = \pi r^2$ Area of a circle
$= \pi(6)^2$ $r = 6$
≈ 113.1 Simplify.

The total area is the lateral area plus the area of the two bases.
$T = 527.8 + 113.1 + 113.1$ or 754 square centimeters.

Exercises

Find the surface area of each cylinder. Round to the nearest tenth.

1.
10 in., 12 in.
603.2 in²

2. 2 m, 2 m
50.3 m²

3. 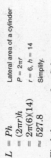 3 yd, 2 yd
94.2 yd²

4. 8 in., 12 in.
1005.3 in²

5. 2 m, 15 m
213.6 m²

6. 8 in., 20 in.
1407.4 in²

Chapter 12   22   Glencoe Geometry

12-3 Skills Practice

NAME _____ DATE _____ PERIOD _____

Surface Areas of Cylinders

Find the surface area of a cylinder with the given dimensions. Round to the nearest tenth.

1. $r = 10$ in., $h = 12$ in.
1382.3 in²

2. $r = 8$ cm, $h = 15$ cm
1156.1 cm²

3. $r = 5$ ft, $h = 20$ ft
785.4 ft²

4. $d = 20$ yd, $h = 5$ yd
942.5 yd²

5. $d = 8$ m, $h = 7$ m
276.5 m²

6. $d = 24$ mm, $h = 20$ mm
2412.7 mm²

Find the surface area of each cylinder. Round to the nearest tenth.

7. 5 ft, 7 ft
377.0 ft²

8. 4 m, 8.5 m
131.9 m²

Find the radius of the base of each cylinder.

9. The surface area is 603.2 square meters, and the height is 10 meters.
6 m

10. The surface area is 100.5 square inches, and the height is 6 inches.
2 in.

11. The surface area is 226.2 square centimeters, and the height is 5 centimeters.
4 cm

12. The surface area is 1520.5 square yards, and the height is 14.2 yards.
10 yd

Chapter 12   23   Glencoe Geometry

Answers (Lesson 12–3)

12-3 Practice

Surface Areas of Cylinders

Find the surface area of a cylinder with the given dimensions. Round to the nearest tenth.

1. $r = 8$ cm, $h = 9$ cm
   854.5 cm²

2. $r = 12$ in., $h = 14$ in.
   1960.4 in²

3. $d = 14$ mm, $h = 32$ mm
   1715.3 mm²

4. $d = 6$ yd, $h = 12$ yd
   282.7 yd²

5. $r = 2.5$ ft, $h = 7$ ft
   149.2 ft²

6. $d = 13$ m, $h = 20$ m
   1082.3 m²

Find the surface area of each cylinder. Round to the nearest tenth.

7.
   19 in.
   17 in.
   1581.8 in²

8.
   12 m
   30 m
   3166.7 m²

Find the radius of the base of each right cylinder.

9. The surface area is 628.3 square millimeters, and the height is 15 millimeters.
   5 mm

10. The surface area is 892.2 square feet, and the height is 4.2 feet.
    10 ft

11. The surface area is 158.3 square inches, and the height is 5.4 inches.
    3 in.

12. **KALEIDOSCOPES** Nathan built a kaleidoscope with a 20-centimeter barrel and a 5-centimeter diameter. He plans to cover the barrel with embossed paper of his own design. How many square centimeters of paper will it take to cover the barrel of the kaleidoscope?
    about 314.2 cm²

Chapter 12   24   Glencoe Geometry

12-3 Word Problem Practice

Surface Areas of Cylinders

1. **DRUMS** A drum is shaped like a cylinder with a height of 5 inches and a radius of 7 inches. What is the surface area of the drum? Round your answer to the nearest hundredth.
   527.79 in²

2. **DRINKING GLASSES** A drinking glass is shaped like a cylinder with a height of 7 inches and a diameter of 3 inches.

   What is the surface area of the drinking glass? Remember that the glass has an open top. Round your answer to the nearest hundredth.
   73.04 in²

3. **ORIGAMI** Hank takes a square sheet of paper and rolls it into a cylinder. The square is 10 inches by 10 inches.

   What are the dimensions of the cylinder and what is the lateral area of the cylinder? Round your answers to the nearest hundredth.
   The cylinder has a height of 10 in. and a radius of 1.59 in.; the lateral surface area is 100 in²

4. **EXHAUST PIPES** An exhaust pipe is shaped like a cylinder with a height of 50 inches and a radius of 2 inches. What is the lateral surface area of the exhaust pipe? Round your answer to the nearest hundredth.
   628.32 in²

TOWERS For Exercises 5 and 6, use the following information.

A circular tower is made by placing one cylinder on top of another. Both cylinders have a height of 18 inches. The top cylinder has a radius of 18 inches and the bottom cylinder has a radius of 36 inches.

18 in.
18 in.

5. What is the total surface area of the tower? Round your answer to the nearest hundredth.
   14,250.26 in²

6. Another tower is constructed by placing the original tower on top of another cylinder with a height of 18 inches and a radius of 54 inches. What is the total surface area of the new tower? Round your answer to the nearest hundredth.
   30,536.28 in²

Chapter 12   25   Glencoe Geometry

Answers

12-3 Enrichment

NAME _____ DATE _____ PERIOD _____

Minimizing Cost in Manufacturing

Suppose that a manufacturer wants to make a can that has a volume of 40 cubic inches. The cost to make the can is 3 cents per square inch for the top and bottom and 1 cent per square inch for the side.

1. Write the value of h in terms of r. $h = \dfrac{40}{\pi r^2}$

2. Write a formula for the cost in terms of r.
$C = 3(2\pi r^2) + 1\left(2\pi r \cdot \dfrac{40}{\pi r^2}\right)$ or $6\pi r^2 + \dfrac{80}{r}$

3. Use a graphing calculator to graph the formula, letting Y_1 represent the cost and X represent r. Use the graph to estimate the point at which the cost is minimized. **the minimum height is 7.71 in. which gives a minimum cost of 93¢.**

4. Repeat the procedure using 2 cents per square inch for the top and bottom and 4 cents per square inch for the top and bottom.
2 cents: $C = 4\pi r^2 + \dfrac{80}{r}$ $h = 5.88$ in.; **4 cents:** $C = 8\pi r^2 + \dfrac{80}{r}$ $h = 9.34$ in.

5. What would you expect to happen as the cost of the top and bottom increases? **See students' work. Sample answer: The manufacturer might make the cans taller and narrower.**

6. Compute the table for the cost value given. What happens to the height of the can as the cost of the top and bottom increases?
The height increases as the cost of the top and bottom go up.

Cost Top & Bottom	Cost Cylinder	Minimum h
2 cents	1 cent	5.88
3 cents	1 cent	7.71
4 cents	1 cent	9.34
5 cents	1 cent	10.84
6 cents	1 cent	12.24

12-3 Spreadsheet Activity

NAME _____ DATE _____ PERIOD _____

Surface Areas of Cylinders

You can use a spreadsheet to determine the surface area of a cylinder.

Example 1 Lucy wants to wrap a Mother's Day gift. The gift she has bought for her mother is in a cylindrical box that is 6 inches tall and has a radius of 3 inches. The cost to make wrapping paper to buy. Use a spreadsheet to determine the surface area of the box. Round to the nearest tenth.

Step 1 Use cell A1 for the radius of the cylinder and cell B1 for the height.

Step 2 In cell C1, enter an equals sign followed by 2*PI()*A1*B1+2*PI()*A1^2. Then press ENTER. This will return the surface area of the cylinder.

The surface area of the cylindrical box is 169.6 in² to the nearest tenth.

	A	B	C
1	3	6	169.646
2	2.5	5.2	120.9513

Sheet 1

Example 2 Use a spreadsheet to determine the surface area of a cylinder that has a radius of 2.5 centimeters and a height of 5.2 centimeters. Round to the nearest tenth.

Step 1 Use cell A2 for the radius of the cylinder and cell B2 for the height.

Step 2 Click on the bottom right corner of cell C1 and drag it to C2. This returns the surface area of the cylinder.

The surface area of the cylinder is 121.0 cm² to the nearest tenth.

Exercises heet to find the surface area of each cylinder with the given dimensions. Round to the nearest tenth.

1. $r = 12$ m, $h = 2.3$ m
1078.2 m²

2. $r = 6$ m, $h = 2$ m
301.6 m²

3. $r = 3$ in., $h = 7$ in.
188.5 in²

4. $r = 5$ in., $h = 11$ in.
502.7 in²

5. $r = 1$ ft, $h = 3$ ft
25.1 ft²

6. $r = 3$ ft, $h = 1.5$ ft
84.8 ft²

7. $r = 10$ mm, $h = 20$ mm
1885.0 mm²

8. $r = 1.5$ mm, $h = 4.5$ mm
56.5 mm²

9. $r = 6.2$ cm, $h = 1.2$ cm
288.3 cm²

10. $r = 10$ cm, $h = 15$ cm
1570.8 cm²

11. $r = 10$ m, $h = 2$ m
754.0 m²

12. $r = 11$ m, $h = 13$ m
1658.8 m²

Answers (Lesson 12–4)

12-4 Lesson Reading Guide

Surface Areas of Pyramids

Get Ready for the Lesson

Read the introduction to Lesson 12-4 in your textbook.

Why do you think that the architect for the new entrance to the Louvre decided to use a pyramid rather than a rectangular prism?

Sample answer: The pyramid, with its sharp point at the vertex and its sloping sides, is more unusual and dramatic than a rectangular prism.

Read the Lesson

1. In the figure, *ABCDE* has congruent sides and congruent angles.

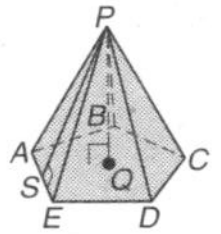

a. Describe this pyramid with as specific a name as possible. **regular pentagonal pyramid**

b. Use the figure to name the base of this pyramid. ***ABCDE***

c. Describe the base of the pyramid. **regular pentagon**

d. Name the vertex of the pyramid. ***P***

e. Name the lateral faces of the pyramid. △*PAB*, △*PBC*, △*PCD*, △*PDE*, and △*PEA*

f. Describe the lateral faces. **five congruent isosceles triangles**

g. Name the lateral edges of the pyramid. $\overline{PA}, \overline{PB}, \overline{PC}, \overline{PD},$ and $\overline{PE}$

h. Name the altitude of the pyramid. $\overline{PQ}$

i. Write an expression for the height of the pyramid. *PQ*

j. Write an expression for the slant height of the pyramid. *PS*

2. In a regular square pyramid, let *s* represent the side length of the base, *h* represent the height, *a* represent the apothem, and ℓ represent the slant height. Also, let *L* represent the lateral area and let *T* represent the surface area. Which of the following relationships are correct? **A, D, E, F**

A. $s = 2a$ 　　B. $a^2 + \ell^2 = h^2$ 　　C. $L = 4\ell s$

D. $h = \sqrt{\ell^2 - a^2}$ 　E. $\left(\frac{s}{2}\right)^2 + h^2 = \ell^2$ 　F. $T = s^2 + 2\ell s$

Remember What You Learned

3. A good way to remember something is to explain it to someone else. Suppose that one of your classmates is having trouble remembering the difference between the *height* and the *slant height* of a regular pyramid. How can you explain this concept?

Sample answer: The *height* of the pyramid is the length of the perpendicular segment from the vertex to the center of the base. The *slant height* is the length of the perpendicular segment from the vertex of the pyramid to the midpoint of one of the sides of the base of the pyramid.

12-4 Study Guide and Intervention

Surface Areas of Pyramids

Lateral Areas of Regular Pyramids Here are some properties of pyramids.

- The base is a polygon.
- All of the faces, except the base, intersect in a common point known as the **vertex**.
- The faces that intersect at the vertex, which are called **lateral faces**, are triangles.

For a **regular pyramid**, the base is a regular polygon and the **slant height** is the height of each lateral face.

Lateral Area of a Regular Pyramid	If a regular pyramid has a lateral area of *L* square units, a slant height of ℓ units, and its base has a perimeter of *P* units, then $L = \frac{1}{2}P\ell$.

Example The roof of a barn is a regular octagonal pyramid. The base of the pyramid has sides of 12 feet, and the slant height of the roof is 15 feet. Find the lateral area of the roof.

The perimeter of the base is 8(12) or 96 feet.

$L = \frac{1}{2}P\ell$ 　　Lateral area of a pyramid

$= \frac{1}{2}(96)(15)$ 　$P = 96, \ \ell = 15$

$= 720$ 　　Multiply.

The lateral area is 720 square feet.

Exercises

Find the lateral area of each regular pyramid. Round to the nearest tenth if necessary.

1.

15 cm　8 cm　8 cm　8 cm

180 cm²

2.

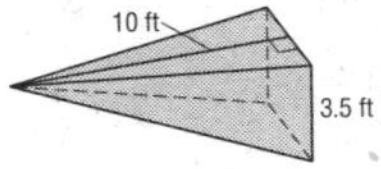

10 ft　3.5 ft

70 ft²

3.

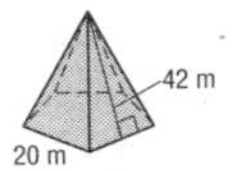

20 m　42 m

2100 m²

4.

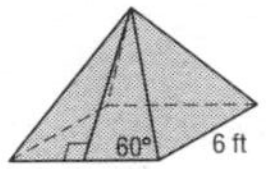

60°　6 ft

62.4 ft²

5.

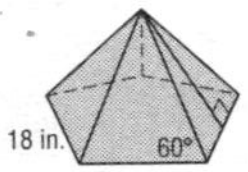

18 in.　60°

701.5 in²

6.

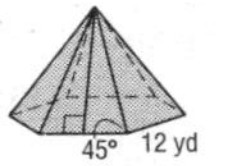

45°　12 yd

216 yd²

Chapter 12

12-4 Study Guide and Intervention *(continued)*

Surface Areas of Pyramids

Surface Areas of Regular Pyramids The surface area of a regular pyramid is the lateral area plus the area of the base.

Surface Area of a Regular Pyramid	If a regular pyramid has a surface area of T square units, a slant height of ℓ units, and its base has a perimeter of P units and an area of B square units, then $T = \frac{1}{2}P\ell + B$.

Example For the regular square pyramid above, find the surface area to the nearest tenth if each side of the base is 12 centimeters and the height of the pyramid is 8 centimeters.

Look at the pyramid above. The slant height is the hypotenuse of a right triangle. One leg of that triangle is the height of the pyramid, and the other leg is half the length of a side of the base. Use the Pythagorean Theorem to find the slant height ℓ.

$\ell^2 = 6^2 + 8^2$ Pythagorean Theorem
$= 100$ Simplify.
$\ell = 10$ Take the square root of each side.

$T = \frac{1}{2}P\ell + B$ Surface area of a pyramid
$= \frac{1}{2}(4)(12)(10) + 12^2$ $P = (4)(12), \ell = 10, B = 12^2$
$= 384$ Simplify.

The surface area is 384 square centimeters.

Exercises

Find the surface area of each regular pyramid. Round to the nearest tenth if necessary.

1. 547.4 cm²
2. 618.0 ft²
3. 400 cm²
4. 456.8 in²
5. 360 cm²
6. 340 yd²

12-4 Skills Practice

Surface Areas of Pyramids

Find the surface area of each regular pyramid. Round to the nearest tenth if necessary.

1. 72 cm²
2. 646.3 in²
3. 455.3 m²
4. 585.0 ft²
5. 98.1 mm²
6. 120 yd²
7. 864 m²
8. 945.3 in²

Left Page

NAME _____ DATE _____ PERIOD _____

12-4 Practice

Surface Areas of Pyramids

Find the surface area of each regular pyramid. **Round to the nearest tenth if necessary.**

1.

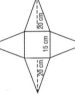

261 yd²

2.

147.2 m²

3.

205.5 ft²

4.

76.2 cm²

5.

322.2 in²

6.

784.7 mm²

7.

75.7 yd²

8.

130.1 m²

9. GAZEBOS The roof of a gazebo is a regular octagonal pyramid. If the base of the pyramid has sides of 0.5 meters and the slant height of the roof is 1.9 meters, find the area of the roof.

3.8 m²

Right Page

NAME _____ DATE _____ PERIOD _____

12-4 Word Problem Practice

Surface Areas of Pyramids

1. PAPER MODELS Patrick is making a paper model of a castle. Part of the model involves cutting out the net shown and folding it into a pyramid. The pyramid has a square base. What is the lateral surface area of the resulting pyramid?

600 cm²

2. TETRAHEDRON Sung Li builds a paper model of a regular tetrahedron, a pyramid with an equilateral triangle for the base and three equilateral triangles for the lateral faces. One of the faces of the tetrahedron has an area of 17 square inches. What is the total surface area of the tetrahedron?

68 in²

3. PAPERWEIGHTS Daphne uses a paperweight shaped like a pyramid with a regular hexagon for a base. The side length of the regular hexagon is 1 inch. The altitude of the pyramid is 2 inches.

What is the lateral surface area of this pyramid? Round your answers to the nearest hundredth.

6.54 in²

4. DICE A game needs random numbers between 1 and 8, inclusive. For that reason, the game uses a die in the shape of a regular octahedron. (A regular octahedron can be made by attaching two square pyramids together along their bases.) The lateral faces are congruent equilateral triangles with side length 2 centimeters. What is the surface area of the die?

Round your answer to the nearest hundredth.
13.86 cm²

CHEESE For Exercises 5 and 6, use the following information.

A piece of goat cheese is sold in the shape of a square pyramid. The base has a side length of 4 inches and the altitude is 3 inches. Round your answers to the nearest hundredth.

5. Caroline cuts off the tip of the cheese by slicing the pyramid along a plane parallel to the base resulting in a smaller square pyramid with an altitude of 1 inch. What is the surface area of this cheese tip?

4.98 in²

6. What is the surface area of the remaining part of the cheese?

41.64 in²

Answers

12-4 Enrichment

NAME _____ DATE _____ PERIOD _____

Two Truncated Solids

To create a truncated solid, you could start with an ordinary solid and then cut off the corners. Another way to make such a shape is to use the patterns on this page.

The Truncated Octahedron

1. Two copies of the pattern at the right can be used to make a *truncated octahedron*, a solid with 6 square faces and 8 regular hexagonal faces.

   Each pattern makes half of the truncated octahedron. Attach adjacent faces using glue or tape to make a cup-shaped figure.

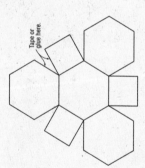

Tape or glue here.

The Truncated Tetrahedron

2. The pattern below will make a *truncated tetrahedron*, a solid with 8 polygonal faces: 4 hexagons and 4 equilateral triangles.

Solve.

3. Find the surface area of the truncated octahedron if each polygon in the pattern has sides of 3 inches.

   241.1 in²

4. Find the surface area of the truncated tetrahedron if each polygon in the pattern has sides of 3 inches.

   109.1 in²

Area Formulas for Regular Polygons		
(s is the length of one side)		
triangle	$A = \dfrac{s^2}{4}\sqrt{3}$	
hexagon	$A = \dfrac{3s^2}{2}\sqrt{3}$	
octagon	$A = 2s^2(\sqrt{2}+1)$	

12-5 Lesson Reading Guide

NAME _____ DATE _____ PERIOD _____

Surface Areas of Cones

Get Ready for the Lesson

Read the introduction to Lesson 12-5 in your textbook.

If you wanted to build a tepee of a certain size, how would it help you to know the formula for the lateral area of a cone?

Sample answer: The formula would help you estimate how many animal skins you would need for the tepee.

Read the Lesson

1.

Net A   Net B   Net C

a. Which net will give the cone with the greatest lateral area?   **Net B**

b. Which net will give the tallest cone?   **Net C**

2. Refer to the figure at the right. Suppose you have removed the circular base of the cone and cut from V to A so that you can unroll the lateral surface onto a flat table.

a. How can you be sure that the flattened-out piece is a sector of a circle?

   Sample answer: Before you unroll the lateral surface, all points on the bottom rim of the cone are ℓ units from V. After you flatten out the surface, those points are still ℓ units from V. This means that they will lie on a circle with center V and radius ℓ.

b. How do you know that the flattened-out piece is not a full circle?

   Sample answer: $r < \ell$

3. Suppose you have a right cone with radius r, diameter d, height h, and slant height ℓ. Which of the following relationships involving these lengths are correct?   **C, E**

   A. $r = 2d$ B. $r + h = \ell$ C. $r^2 + h^2 = \ell^2$

   D. $r^2 + \ell^2 = h^2$ E. $r = \sqrt{\ell^2 - h^2}$ F. $h = \pm\sqrt{\ell^2 - r^2}$

Remember What You Learned

4. One way to remember a new formula is to relate it to a formula you already know. Explain how the formulas for the lateral areas of a pyramid and a cone are similar.

   Sample answer: Both formulas say that the lateral area includes the distance around the base multiplied by the slant height.

Left Page

12-5 Study Guide and Intervention (continued)

Surface Areas of Cones

Lateral Areas of Cones Cones have the following properties.

- A cone has one circular base and one vertex.
- The segment whose endpoints are the vertex and the center of the base is the **axis** of the cone.
- The segment that has one endpoint at the vertex, is perpendicular to the base, and has its other endpoint on the base is the **altitude** of the cone.
- For a **right cone** the axis is also the altitude, and any segment from the vertex to the base is the **slant height**. If a cone is not a right cone, it is oblique.

| Lateral Area of a Cone | If a cone has a lateral area of L square units, a slant height of ℓ units, and the radius of the base is r units, then $L = \pi r \ell$. |

Example Find the lateral area of a cone with slant height of 10 centimeters and a base with a radius of 6 centimeters.

$L = \pi r \ell$ Lateral area of a cone
$= \pi(6)(10)$ $r = 6, \ell = 10$
≈ 188.5 Simplify.

The lateral area is about 188.5 square centimeters.

Exercises

Find lateral area of each cone. Round to the nearest tenth.

1.
47.1 cm²

2.
424.1 cm²

3.
391.8 m²

4.
816.8 mm²

5.
204.2 in²

6.
234.3 yd²

Right Page

12-5 Study Guide and Intervention (continued)

Surface Areas of Cones

Surface Areas of Cones The surface area of a cone is the lateral area of the cone plus the area of the base.

| Surface Area of a Right Cone | If a cone has a surface area of T square units, a slant height of ℓ units, and the radius of the base is r units, then $T = \pi r \ell + \pi r^2$. |

Example For the cone above, find the surface area to the nearest tenth if the radius is 6 centimeters and the height is 8 centimeters.

The slant height is the hypotenuse of a right triangle with legs of length 6 and 8. Use the Pythagorean Theorem.

$\ell^2 = 6^2 + 8^2$ Pythagorean Theorem
$\ell^2 = 100$ Simplify.
$\ell = 10$ Take the square root of each side.

$T = \pi r \ell + \pi r^2$ Surface area of a cone
$= \pi(6)(10) + \pi \cdot 6^2$ $r = 6, \ell = 10$
≈ 301.6 Simplify.

The surface area is about 301.6 square centimeters.

Exercises

Find the surface area of each cone. Round to the nearest tenth.

1.
678.6 cm²

2.
235.6 ft²

3.
282.7 cm²

4.
121.4 in²

5.
2890.3 m²

6.
603.2 yd²

NAME ______________________ DATE ____________ PERIOD _____

12-5 Skills Practice

Surface Areas of Cones

Find the surface area of each cone. Round to the nearest tenth if necessary.

1. 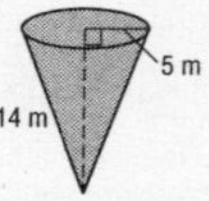
5 m
14 m

298.5 m^2

2. 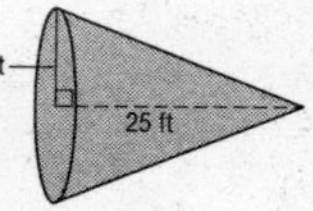
10 ft
25 ft

1160.1 ft^2

3. 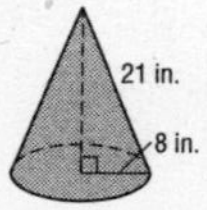
21 in.
8 in.

728.8 in^2

4. 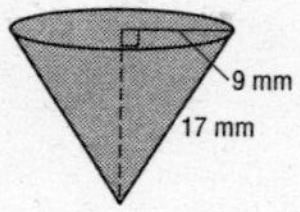
9 mm
17 mm

735.1 mm^2

5. 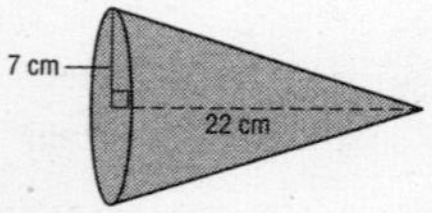
7 cm
22 cm

661.6 cm^2

6. 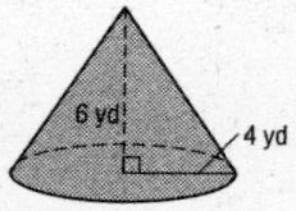
6 yd
4 yd

140.9 yd^2

7. Find the surface area of a cone if the height is 12 inches and the slant height is 15 inches.
678.6 in^2

8. Find the surface area of a cone if the height is 9 centimeters and the slant height is 12 centimeters.
497.1 cm^2

9. Find the surface area of a cone if the height is 10 meters and the slant height is 14 meters.
732.5 m^2

10. Find the surface area of a cone if the height is 5 feet and the slant height is 7 feet.
183.1 ft^2

NAME ______________________ DATE ____________ PERIOD _____

12-5 Practice

Surface Areas of Cones

Find the surface area of each cone. Round to the nearest tenth if necessary.

1. 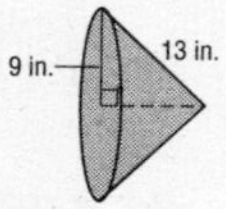
9 in.
13 in.

622.0 in^2

2. 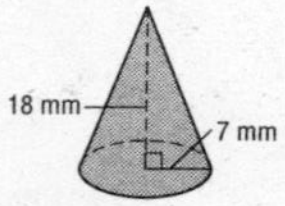
18 mm
7 mm

578.7 mm^2

3. 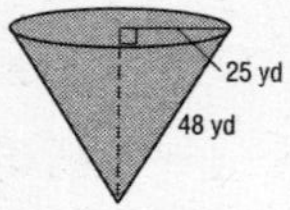
25 yd
48 yd

5733.4 yd^2

4. 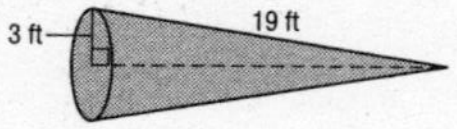
3 ft
19 ft

207.3 ft^2

5. 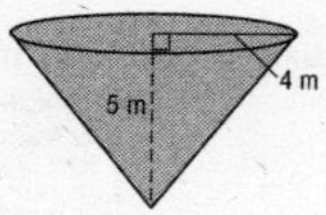
5 m
4 m

130.7 m^2

6. 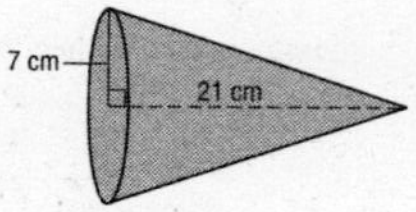
7 cm
21 cm

640.7 cm^2

7. Find the surface area of a cone if the height is 8 feet and the slant height is 10 feet.
301.6 ft^2

8. Find the surface area of a cone if the height is 14 centimeters and the slant height is 16.4 centimeters.
669.3 cm^2

9. Find the surface area of a cone if the height is 12 inches and the diameter is 27 inches.
1338.6 in^2

10. HATS Cuong bought a conical hat on a recent trip to central Vietnam. The basic frame of the hat is 16 hoops of bamboo that gradually diminish in size. The hat is covered in palm leaves. If the hat has a diameter of 50 centimeters and a slant height of 32 centimeters, what is the lateral area of the conical hat?
about 2513.3 cm^2

Lesson 12-5

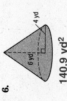

Answers (Lesson 12–5)

NAME _____ DATE _____ PERIOD _____

12-5 Word Problem Practice

Surface Areas of Cones

1. **HALF CIRCLES** Charles cuts out a semicircle with a radius of 5 inches from a piece of paper. He then curls it into a cone by joining the two radii on the edge of the semicircle together.

What is the lateral surface area of the resulting cone? Round your answer to the nearest hundredth. **39.27 in²**

2. **CASTLES** A right circular cone with an altitude of 20 feet and a radius of 6 feet serves as the highest cap of a castle.

What is the lateral surface area of this cone? Round your answer to the nearest hundredth. **393.59 ft²**

3. **PAINTING** Naomi is asked to paint a number of congruent cones. She is told that the radius of the cones is 6 inches and the altitude of the cones is 2 inches. What is the surface area of one of the cones? Round your answer to the nearest hundredth. **232.31 in²**

4. **SPRAY PAINT** A can of spray paint shoots out paint in a cone shaped mist. The lateral surface area of the cone is 65π square inches when the can is held 12 inches from a canvas. What is the area of the part of the canvas that gets sprayed with paint? Round your answer to the nearest hundredth. **78.54 in²**

MEGAPHONES For Exercises 5-7, use the following information.

A megaphone is formed by taking a cone with a radius of 20 centimeters and an altitude of 60 centimeters and cutting off the tip. The cut is made along a plane that is perpendicular to the axis of the cone and intersects the axis 12 centimeters from the vertex. Round your answer to the nearest hundredth

5. What is the lateral surface area of the original cone? **3973.84 in²**

6. What is the lateral surface area of the tip that is removed? **158.95 in²**

7. What is the lateral surface area of the megaphone? **3814.88 in²**

NAME _____ DATE _____ PERIOD _____

12-5 Enrichment

Cone Patterns

The pattern at the right is made from a circle. It can be folded to make a cone.

1. Measure the radius of the circle to the nearest centimeter. **4 cm**

2. The pattern is what fraction of the complete circle? $\frac{3}{4}$

3. What is the circumference of the complete circle? **8π cm**

4. How long is the circular arc that is the outside of the pattern? **6π cm**

5. Cut out the pattern and tape it together to form a cone. **See students' work.**

6. Measure the diameter of the circular base of the cone. **6 cm**

7. What is the circumference of the base of the cone? **6π cm**

8. What is the slant height of the cone? **4 cm**

9. Use the Pythagorean Theorem to calculate the height of the cone. Use a decimal approximation. Check your calculation by measuring the height with a metric ruler. **2.65 cm**

10. Find the lateral area. **12π cm²**

11. Find the total surface area. **21π cm²**

Make a paper pattern for each cone with the given measurements. Then cut the pattern out and make the cone. Find the measurements.

12.

diameter of base = **8 cm**

lateral area = **24π cm²**

height of cone = **4.5 cm**
(to nearest tenth of a centimeter)

13.

diameter of base = **10 cm**

lateral area = **50π cm²**

height of cone = **8.7 cm**
(to nearest tenth of a centimeter)

Answers

NAME _____ DATE _____ PERIOD _____

12-6 Lesson Reading Guide

Surface Areas of Spheres

Get Ready for the Lesson

Read the introduction to Lesson 12-6 in your textbook.

How would knowing the formula for the surface area of a sphere help make the world's largest soccer ball? **The surface area of the ball tells the staff how much material is needed to make the ball.**

Read the Lesson

1. In the figure, P is the center of the sphere. Name each of the following in the figure.

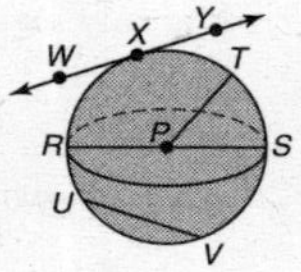

   a. three radii of the sphere $\overline{PT}$, $\overline{PR}$, and $\overline{PS}$

   b. a diameter of the sphere $\overline{RS}$

   c. two chords of the sphere $\overline{RS}$ and $\overline{UV}$

   d. a great circle of the sphere $\odot P$

   e. a tangent to the sphere $\overleftrightarrow{WY}$

   f. the point of tangency X

2. Determine whether each sentence is *sometimes, always,* or *never* true.

   a. If a sphere and a plane intersect in more than one point, their intersection will be a great circle. **sometimes**

   b. A great circle has the same center as the sphere. **always**

   c. The endpoints of a radius of a sphere are two points on the sphere. **never**

   d. A chord of a sphere is a diameter of the sphere. **sometimes**

   e. A radius of a great circle is also a radius of the sphere. **always**

3. Match each surface area formula with the name of the appropriate solid.

   a. $T = \pi r \ell + \pi r^2$ **vi**   i. regular pyramid
   b. $T = Ph + 2B$ **iv**   ii. hemisphere
   c. $T = 4\pi r^2$ **v**   iii. cylinder
   d. $T = \frac{1}{2}P\ell + B$ **i**   iv. prism
   e. $T = 2\pi r h + 2\pi r^2$ **iii**   v. sphere
   f. $T = 3\pi r^2$ **ii**   vi. cone

Remember What You Learned

4. Many students have trouble remembering all of the formulas they have learned in this chapter. What is an easy way to remember the formula for the surface area of a sphere? **Sample answer: A sphere doesn't have any lateral faces or bases, so the expression in the formula for its surface area has just one term, $4\pi r^2$, rather than being the sum of the expressions for the lateral area and the area of the bases like the others.**

NAME _____ DATE _____ PERIOD _____

12-6 Study Guide and Intervention

Surface Areas of Spheres

Properties of Spheres A **sphere** is the locus of all points that are a given distance from a given point called its **center**.

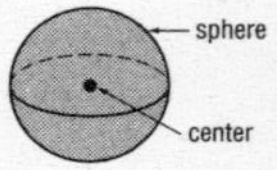

Here are some terms associated with a sphere.

- A **radius** is a segment whose endpoints are the center of the sphere and a point on the sphere.
- A **chord** is a segment whose endpoints are points on the sphere.
- A **diameter** is a chord that contains the sphere's center.
- A **tangent** is a line that intersects the sphere in exactly one point.
- A **great circle** is the intersection of a sphere and a plane that contains the center of the sphere.
- A **hemisphere** is one-half of a sphere. Each great circle of a sphere determines two hemispheres.

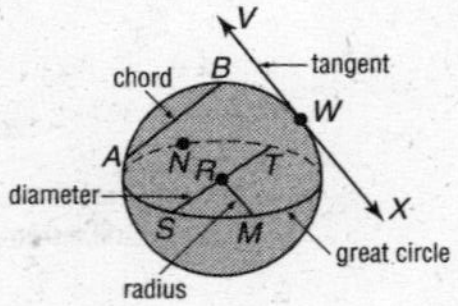

$\overline{RS}$ is a radius. $\overline{AB}$ is a chord.
$\overline{ST}$ is a diameter. $\overleftrightarrow{VX}$ is a tangent.
The circle that contains points S, M, T, and N is a great circle; it determines two hemispheres.

Example Determine the shapes you get when you intersect a plane with a sphere.

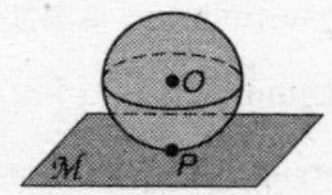

The intersection of plane $\mathcal{M}$ and sphere O is point P.

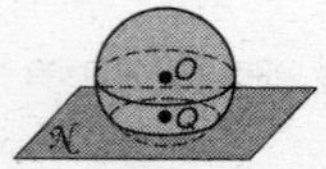

The intersection of plane $\mathcal{X}$ and sphere O is circle Q.

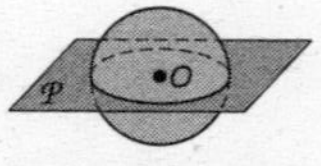

The intersection of plane $\mathcal{P}$ and sphere O is circle O.

A plane can intersect a sphere in a point, in a circle, or in a great circle.

Exercises

Describe each object as a model of a *circle*, a *sphere*, a *hemisphere*, or *none of these*.

1. a baseball   2. a pancake   3. the Earth
   sphere   **circle**   **sphere**

4. a kettle grill cover   5. a basketball rim   6. cola can
   hemisphere   **circle**   **none of these**

Determine whether each statement is *true* or *false*.

7. All lines intersecting a sphere are tangent to the sphere. **false**

8. Every plane that intersects a sphere makes a great circle. **false**

9. The eastern hemisphere of Earth is congruent to the western hemisphere. **true**

10. The diameter of a sphere is congruent to the diameter of a great circle. **true**

Lesson 12-6

NAME _____ DATE _____ PERIOD _____

12-6 Study Guide and Intervention *(continued)*

Surface Areas of Spheres

Surface Areas of Spheres You can think of the surface area of a sphere as the total area of all of the nonoverlapping strips it would take to cover the sphere. If r is the radius of the sphere, then the area of a great circle of the sphere is πr^2. The total surface area of the sphere is four times the area of a great circle.

Surface Area of a Sphere	If a sphere has a surface area of T square units and a radius of r units, then $T = 4\pi r^2$.

Example Find the surface area of a sphere to the nearest tenth if the radius of the sphere is 6 centimeters.

$T = 4\pi r^2$ Surface area of a sphere
$\;\; = 4\pi \cdot 6^2$ $r = 6$
$\;\; \approx 452.4$ Simplify.

The surface area is 452.4 square centimeters.

Exercises

Find the surface area of each sphere with the given radius or diameter to the nearest tenth.

1. $r = 8$ cm
804.2 cm^2

2. $r = 2\sqrt{2}$ ft
100.5 ft^2

3. $r = \pi$ cm
124.0 cm^2

4. $d = 10$ in.
314.2 in^2

5. $d = 6\pi$ m
1116.2 m^2

6. $d = 16$ yd
804.2 yd^2

7. Find the surface area of a hemisphere with radius 12 centimeters.
1357.2 cm^2

8. Find the surface area of a hemisphere with diameter π centimeters.
23.3 cm^2

9. Find the radius of a sphere if the surface area of a hemisphere is 192π square centimeters.
8 cm

Chapter 12 44 *Glencoe Geometry*

NAME _____ DATE _____ PERIOD _____

12-6 Skills Practice

Surface Areas of Spheres

In the figure, A is the center of the sphere, and plane T intersects the sphere in circle E. Round to the nearest tenth if necessary.

1. If $AE = 5$ and $DE = 12$, find AD.
13

2. If $AE = 7$ and $DE = 15$, find AD.
16.6

3. If the radius of the sphere is 18 units and the radius of $\odot E$ is 17 units, find AE.
5.9

4. If the radius of the sphere is 10 units and the radius of $\odot E$ is 9 units, find AE.
4.4

5. If M is a point on $\odot E$ and $AD = 23$, find AM.
23

Find the surface area of each sphere or hemisphere. Round to the nearest tenth.

6.

7 in.

615.8 in^2

7.

32 m

3217.0 m^2

8. a hemisphere with a radius of the great circle 8 yards
603.2 yd^2

9. a hemisphere with a radius of the great circle 2.5 millimeters
58.9 mm^2

10. a sphere with the area of a great circle 28.6 inches
114.4 in^2

Chapter 12 45 *Glencoe Geometry*

Answers (Lesson 12–6)

NAME _____ DATE _____ PERIOD _____

12-6 Practice

Surface Areas of Spheres

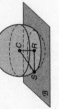

In the figure, C is the center of the sphere, and plane $\mathcal{B}$ intersects the sphere in circle R. Round to the nearest tenth if necessary.

1. If $CR = 4$ and $SR = 14$, find CS.
14.6

2. If $CR = 7$ and $SR = 24$, find CS.
25

3. If the radius of the sphere is 28 units and the radius of $\odot R$ is 26 units, find CR.
10.4

4. If J is a point on $\odot R$ and $CS = 7.3$, find CJ.
7.3

Find the surface area of each sphere or hemisphere. Round to the nearest tenth.

5.

6.5 cm
530.9 cm²

6.
89 ft
24,884.6 ft²

7. a sphere with the area of a great circle 29.8 meters
119.2 m²

8. a hemisphere with a radius of the great circle 8.4 inches
665.0 in²

9. a hemisphere with the circumference of a great circle 18 millimeters
77.3 mm²

10. SPORTS A standard size 5 soccer ball for ages 13 and older has a circumference of 27–28 inches. Suppose Breck is on a team that plays with a 28-inch soccer ball. Find the surface area of the ball.
about 249.6 in²

Chapter 12   46   *Glencoe Geometry*

NAME _____ DATE _____ PERIOD _____

12-6 Word Problem Practice

Surface Areas of Spheres

1. ORANGES Mandy cuts a spherical orange in half along a great circle. If the radius of the orange is 2 inches, what is the area of the cross section that Mandy cut? Round your answer to the nearest hundredth.
12.56 in²

2. COFFEE TABLES A coffee table is made by taking a sphere with a radius of 26 inches and then cutting it along two parallel planes. The two planes are both 10 inches from the center of the sphere. The section of the sphere that contains its center is used as the table.

What is the area of the tabletop?
1808.64 in²

3. MOONS OF SATURN The planet Saturn has several moons. These can be modeled accurately by spheres. Saturn's largest moon Titan has a radius of about 2575 kilometers. What is the approximate surface area of Titan? Round your answer to the nearest tenth.

83,322,891.15 km²

4. METEORS A spherical meteorite lies half exposed in the earth. The diameter of the meteorite is 14 inches. What is the surface area of the exposed surface? Round your answer to the nearest hundredth.
307.88 in²

CUBES For Exercises 5-7, use the following information.
Marcus builds a spherical container for a cube. The cube fits snugly inside the sphere so that the vertices of the cube touch the inside of the sphere. The side length of the cube is 2 inches.

5. What is the surface area of the cube?
24 in²

6. What is the surface area of the sphere? Round your answers to the nearest hundredth.
37.68 in²

7. What is the ratio of the surface area of the cube to the surface area of the sphere? Round your answer to the nearest hundredth.
0.67

Chapter 12   47   *Glencoe Geometry*

NAME _____ DATE _____ PERIOD _____

12-6 Enrichment

Doubling Sizes

Consider what happens to surface area when the sides of a figure are doubled.

The sides of the large cube are twice the size of the sides of the small cube.

1. How long are the edges of the large cube? **10 in.**

2. What is the surface area of the small cube? **150 in^2**

3. What is the surface area of the large cube? **600 in^2**

4. The surface area of the large cube is how many times greater than that of the small cube? **4 times**

The radius of the large sphere at the right is twice the radius of the small sphere.

5. What is the surface area of the small sphere? **36π m^2**

6. What is the surface area of the large sphere? **144π m^2**

7. The surface area of the large sphere is how many times greater than the surface area of the small sphere? **4 times**

8. It appears that if the dimensions of a solid are doubled, the surface area is multiplied by _____. **4**

Now consider how doubling the dimensions affects the volume of a cube.

The sides of the large cube are twice the size of the sides of the small cube.

9. How long are the edges of the large cube? **10 in.**

10. What is the volume of the small cube? **125 in^3**

11. What is the volume of the large cube? **1000 in^3**

12. The volume of the large cube is how many times greater than that of the small cube? **8 times**

The large sphere at the right has twice the radius of the small sphere.

13. What is the volume of the small sphere? **36π m^3**

14. What is the volume of the large sphere? **288π m^3**

15. The volume of the large sphere is how many times greater than the volume of the small sphere? **8 times**

16. It appears that if the dimensions of a solid are doubled, the volume is multiplied by _____. **8**

Chapter 12 Assessment Answer Key

Quiz 1 *(Lessons 12–1 and 12–2)*
Page 51

1.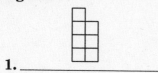

2. Sample answer:

3. __120 units²__

4. __360 cm²__

5. __B__

Quiz 2 *(Lesson 12–3)*
Page 51

1. __100.53 cm²__

2. __12 cm__

3. __rectangle__

4. __3870.4 units²__

5. __4630.7 units²__

Quiz 3 *(Lessons 12–4 and 12–5)*
Page 52

1. __81 units²__

2. __116.1 units²__

3. __260 cm²__

4. __188.5 ft²__

5. __267.0 ft²__

Quiz 4 *(Lesson 12–6)*
Page 52

1. __$\overline{BC}$__

2. __$\overleftrightarrow{AH}$__

3. __$\odot D$__

4. __4071.5 in²__

5. It is multiplied by 4.

Mid-Chapter Test
Page 53

Part I

1. __C__

2. __F__

3. __D__

4. __F__

5. __D__

Part II

6.

7.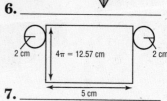

8. __2884 in²__

9. __92.8 units²__

10. __282.7 in²__

Chapter 12 Assessment Answer Key

Vocabulary Test
Page 54

1. slant height

2. perspective view

3. right cylinder

4. hemisphere

5. axis

6. great circle

7. false, pyramid

8. true

9. true

10. false, oblique cone

11. the sum of the areas of the lateral faces

12. a prism whose lateral edges are also altitudes

Form 1
Page 55

1. C

2. F

3. B

4. J

5. B

6. J

7. B

8. J

9. C

10. G

Page 56

11. C

12. F

13. B

14. F

15. B

16. H

17. C

18. G

19. D

20. F

B: 1020 ft^2

Chapter 12 Assessment Answer Key

Form 2A
Page 57

1. D
2. H
3. D
4. H
5. A
6. H
7. B
8. G
9. C
10. J

Page 58

11. A
12. H
13. A
14. F
15. B
16. G
17. C
18. G
19. A
20. F
B: 391.6 ft²

Form 2B
Page 59

1. B
2. J
3. A
4. G
5. D
6. H
7. B
8. G
9. D
10. G

Page 60

11. C
12. F
13. A
14. H
15. D
16. F
17. B
18. G
19. D
20. H
B: 53 ft²

Chapter 12 Assessment Answer Key

Form 2C
Page 61

1.

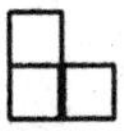

2. $\square PQRS, \triangle PQT,$ $\triangle QTR, \triangle RTS, \triangle PTS$

3. hexagonal pyramid

4. 12

5. Sample answer:

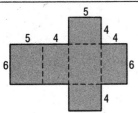

6. 240 in^2

7. 120 cm^2

8. 3536 units^2

9. 7.2 in^2

10. 7 gal

Page 62

11. 524.1 yd^2

12. 6 in.

13. 270 in^2

14. $270 + 150\sqrt{3}$ in^2

15. 144 units^2

16. 56.5 cm

17. 62.8 ft^2

18. 113.1 ft^2

19. 17 m

20. 235.6 cm^2

B: 38.5 in^2

Chapter 12 Assessment Answer Key

Form 2D
Page 63

1.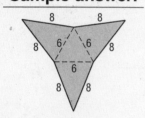

2. $\overline{GJ}$, $\overline{HJ}$, $\overline{IJ}$, $\overline{GH}$, $\overline{HI}$, $\overline{GI}$

3. pentagonal prism

4. 12

5. Sample answer:

6. 840 cm^2

7. 750 in^2

8. 258 ft^2

9. 3 gal

10. 180 in^2

Page 64

11. 845.2 m^2

12. 7 ft

13. 540 ft^2

14. 931.0 ft^2

15. 156.9 units^2

16. 22.4 ft

17. 204.2 cm^2

18. 282.7 cm^2

19. 5 m

20. 1140.4 in^2

B: 113.1 in^2

Chapter 12 Assessment Answer Key

Form 3
Page 65

1. _____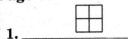

2. $\triangle XYZ$, $\triangle UVW$

3. octahedron

4. 20

5. Sample answer:

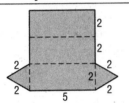

6. $\dfrac{128 + 4\sqrt{21}}{\text{units}^2}$

7. $35 + 7\sqrt{13}$ ft^2

8. 528 units^2

9. 17,837.8 ft^2

10. 32,435.2 ft^2

11. 37.70 in^2

Page 66

12. 468 in^2

13. 842.1 in^2

14. It is multiplied by 9.

15. 233.8 in^2

16. 387.7 in^2

17. 182.0 cm^2

18. $2\sqrt{21}$

19. $3\pi r^2$

20. 1709 ft^2

B: 700 ft^2

Chapter 12 Assessment Answer Key

Extended-Response Test, Page 67
Scoring Rubric

Score	General Description	Specific Criteria
4	**Superior** A correct solution that is supported by well-developed, accurate explanations	• Shows thorough understanding of the concepts of *pyramids, prisms, cylinders, cones, spheres, surface area, lateral area, nets, and properties of solid figures.* • Uses appropriate strategies to solve problems. • Computations are correct. • Written explanations are exemplary. • Figures and drawings are accurate and appropriate. • Goes beyond requirements of some or all problems.
3	**Satisfactory** A generally correct solution, but may contain minor flaws in reasoning or computation	• Shows an understanding of the concepts of *pyramids, prisms, cylinders, cones, spheres, surface area, lateral area, nets, and properties of solid figures.* • Uses appropriate strategies to solve problems. • Computations are mostly correct. • Written explanations are effective. • Figures and drawings are mostly accurate and appropriate. • Satisfies all requirements of problems.
2	**Nearly Satisfactory** A partially correct interpretation and/or solution to the problem	• Shows an understanding of most of the concepts of *pyramids, prisms, cylinders, cones, spheres, surface area, lateral area, nets, and properties of solid figures.* • May not use appropriate strategies to solve problems. • Computations are mostly correct. • Written explanations are satisfactory. • Figures and drawings are mostly accurate. • Satisfies the requirements of most of the problems.
1	**Nearly Unsatisfactory** A correct solution with no supporting evidence or explanation	• Final computation is correct. • No written explanations or work shown to substantiate the final computation. • Figures and drawings may be accurate but lack detail or explanation. • Satisfies minimal requirements of some of the problems.
0	**Unsatisfactory** An incorrect solution indicating no mathematical understanding of the concept or task, or no solution is given	• Shows little or no understanding of most of the concepts of *pyramids, prisms, cylinders, cones, spheres, surface area, lateral area, nets, and properties of solid figures.* • Does not use appropriate strategies to solve problems. • Computations are incorrect. • Written explanations are unsatisfactory. • Figures and drawings are inaccurate or inappropriate. • Does not satisfy requirements of problems. • No answer given.

Chapter 12 Assessment Answer Key

In addition to the scoring rubric found on page A30, the following sample answers may be used as guidance in evaluating open-ended assessment items.

1. a.

Figure	No. of Edges (e)	No. of Faces (f)	No. of Vertices (v)	f + v
Triangular Pyramid	6	4	4	8
Triangular Prism	9	5	6	11
Cube	12	6	8	14
Square Pyramid	8	5	5	10
Hexagonal Prism	18	8	12	20
Hexagonal Pyramid	12	7	7	14

b. $e = f + v - 2$

2. The lateral area is the area of the lateral faces. The surface area includes the area of the lateral faces plus the areas of the two bases.

3. a.

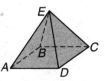

b. $\square ABCD$

c. $\triangle ABE, \triangle BCE, \triangle CDE, \triangle ADE$

d.

4.

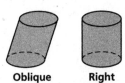

Oblique   Right

5. a.

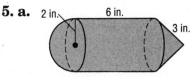

b. 38π in^2

6. Sample answer: Sam is painting the walls of a room. The room is 12 feet long, 10 feet wide, and 8 feet high. A gallon of paint covers 400 square feet and costs $16 per gallon. Find the cost of the paint needed to paint the room.

Answers

Chapter 12 Assessment Answer Key

Standardized Test Practice
Page 68

Page 69

1. Ⓐ ● Ⓒ Ⓓ

2. ● Ⓖ Ⓗ Ⓙ

3. Ⓐ Ⓑ Ⓒ ●

4. Ⓕ Ⓖ Ⓗ ●

5. ● Ⓑ Ⓒ Ⓓ

6. Ⓕ ● Ⓗ Ⓙ

7. Ⓐ Ⓑ ● Ⓓ

8. ● Ⓖ Ⓗ Ⓙ

9. Ⓐ Ⓑ ● Ⓓ

10. Ⓕ Ⓖ Ⓗ ●

11. Ⓐ Ⓑ ● Ⓓ

12. Ⓕ ● Ⓗ Ⓙ

13. **1 4 .**

14. **5 .**

Chapter 12 Assessment Answer Key

Standardized Test Practice
Page 70

15. _____ 2.6 m _____

16. _____ 25 _____

17. _____ 51.4 cm^2 _____

18. _____ pentagonal pyramid _____

19. _____ 3141.6 in^2 _____

20. _____ 2206.2 cm^2 _____

21a. _____ 13684.8 m^2 _____

21b. _____ 207.3 m _____

21c. _____ 3421.2 m^2 _____

21d. _____ 10,263.6 m^2 _____